COLDPLAY X&Y

Wise Publications
part of The Music Sales Group
London/New York/Paris/Sydney/Copenhagen/Berlin/Madrid/Tokyo

Published by
Wise Publications,
8/9 Frith Street, London, W1D 3JB, England.

Exclusive distributors:
Music Sales Limited,
Distribution Centre, Newmarket Road, Bury St Edmunds,
Suffolk, IP33 3YB, England.

Music Sales Pty Limited,
120 Rothschild Avenue, Rosebery,
NSW 2018, Australia.

Order No. AM92346
ISBN 0-7119-4422-9

Management by Estelle Wilkinson and Dave Holmes.

Music arrangements by Martin Shellard.
Music processed by Paul Ewers Music Design.
Edited by David Weston.
Original Design and Art Direction: Tappin Gofton.
Photography: Kevin Westenberg, Tom Sheehan and Coldplay.

Printed in the United Kingdom.

www.musicsales.com

SQUARE ONE

Words & Music by Guy Berryman, Jon Buckland, Will Champion & Chris Martin

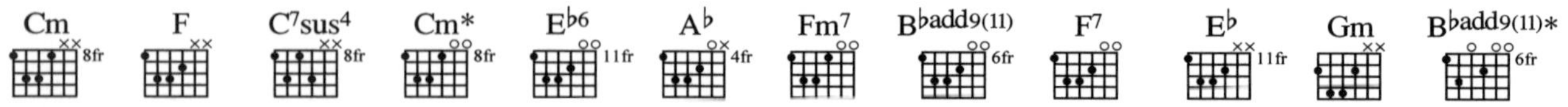

All Gtrs.
6 = E 3 = G
5 = A 2 = C
4 = D 1 = D♯

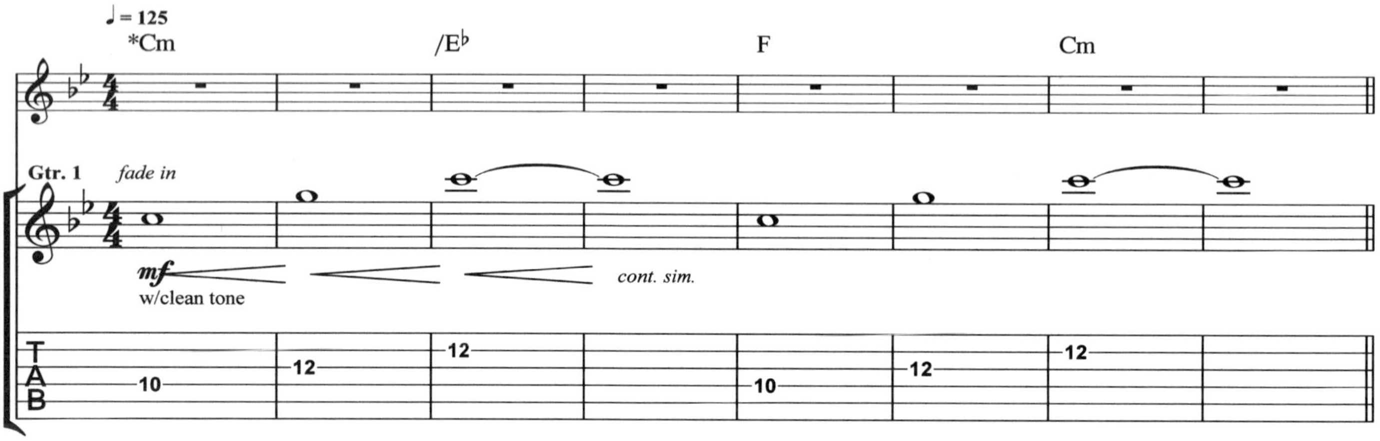

*chords implied by harmony
** w/delay + reverb

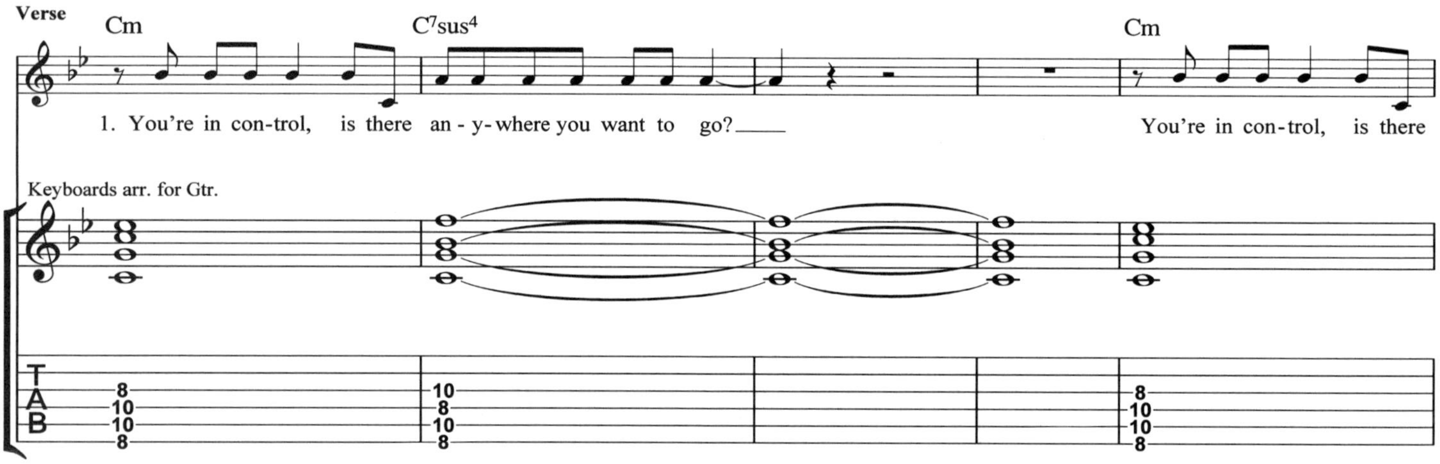

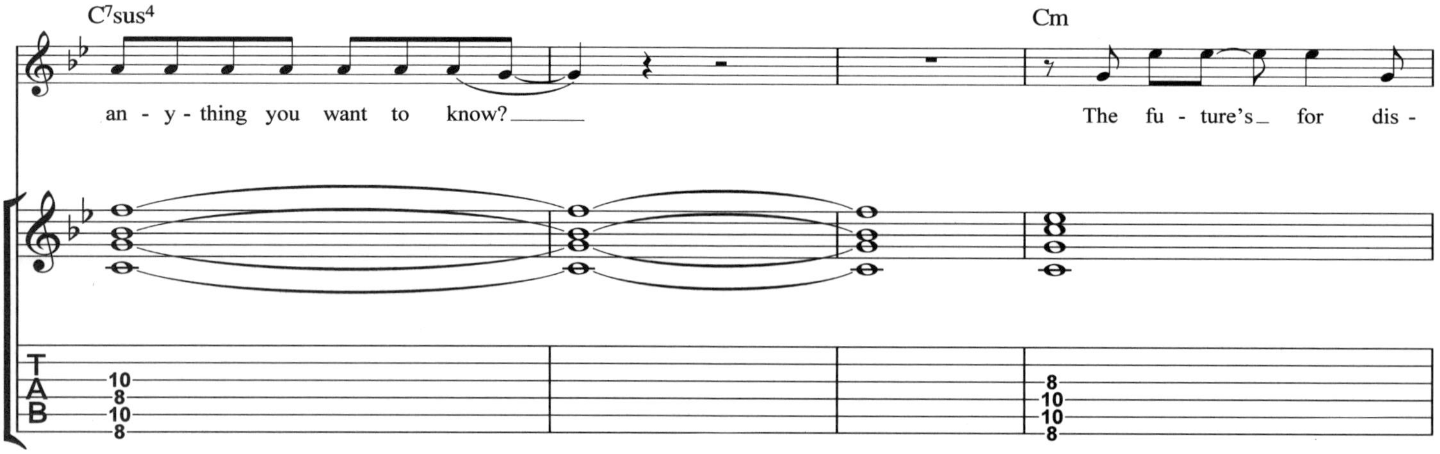

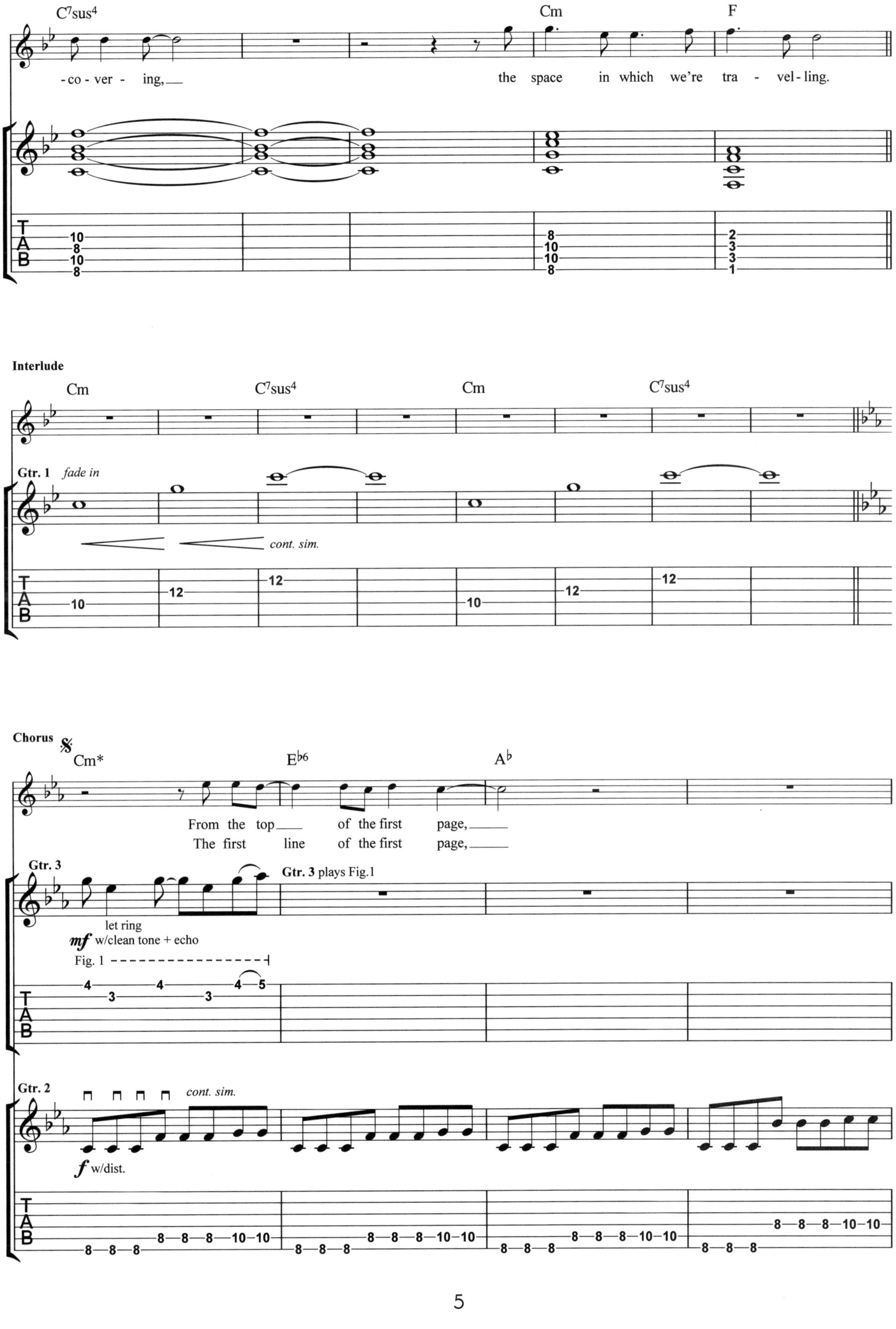
C7sus4
Cm
F
-co - ver - ing,
the space in which we're tra - vel - ling.
T
A
B
Interlude
Cm
C7sus4
Cm
C7sus4
Gtr. 1 fade in
cont. sim.
Chorus
Cm*
E♭6
A♭
From the top of the first page,
The first line of the first page,
Gtr. 3
Gtr. 3 plays Fig. 1
let ring
mf w/clean tone + echo
Fig. 1
Gtr. 2
cont. sim.
f w/dist.

Cm*
Eb6
Fm7
to the end of the last day.
to the end of the last place,
you were look-ing.
Cm*
Eb6
Ab
From the start, in your own way,
you just want
Bbadd9(11)
Ab
some-bo-dy lis-ten-ing to what you say.
It does-n't mat-ter who you
To Coda
F7
are.

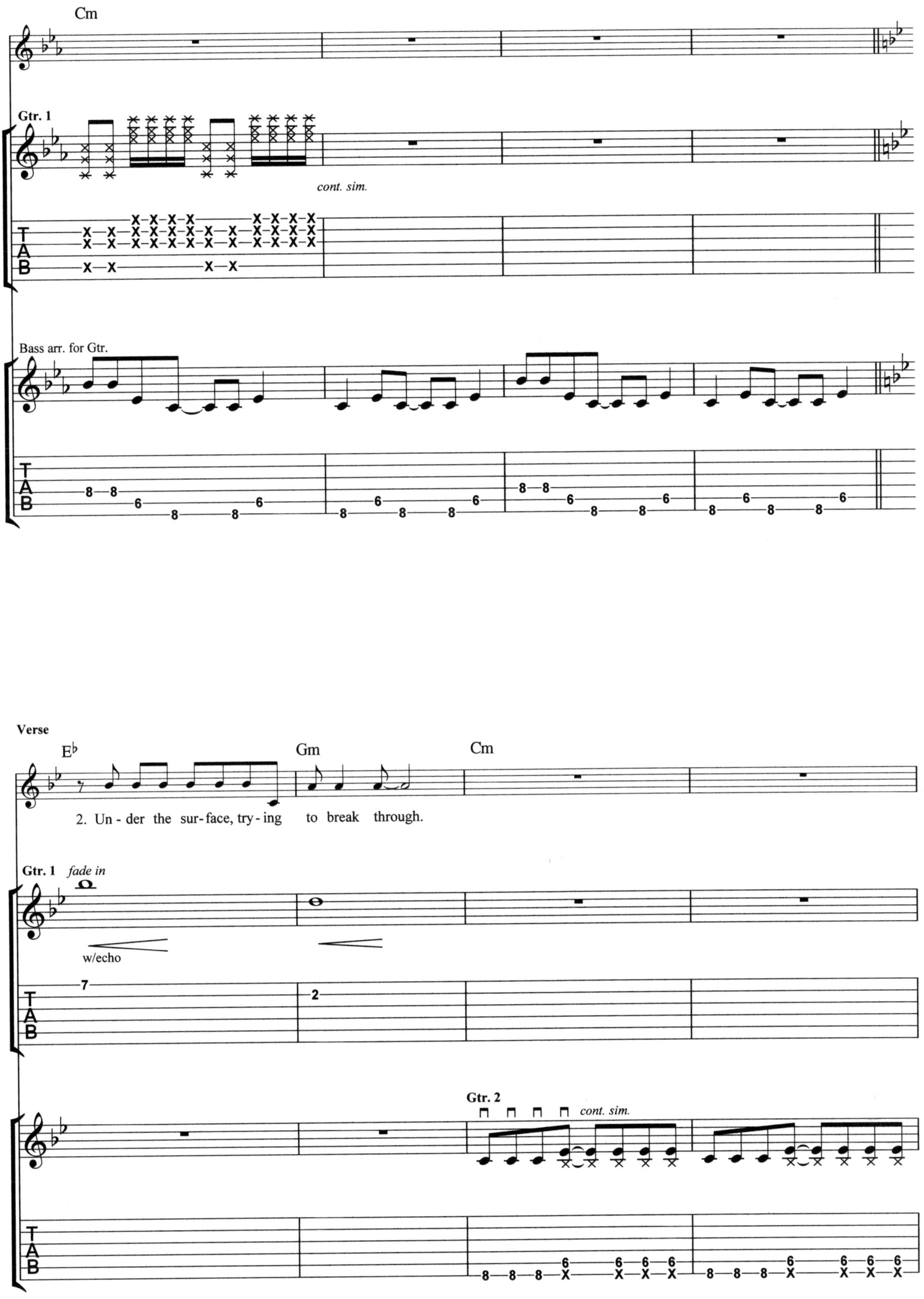
Cm
Gtr. 1
cont. sim.
Bass arr. for Gtr.
Verse
E♭
Gm
Cm
2. Un - der the sur - face, try - ing to break through.
Gtr. 1 fade in
w/echo
Gtr. 2
cont. sim.

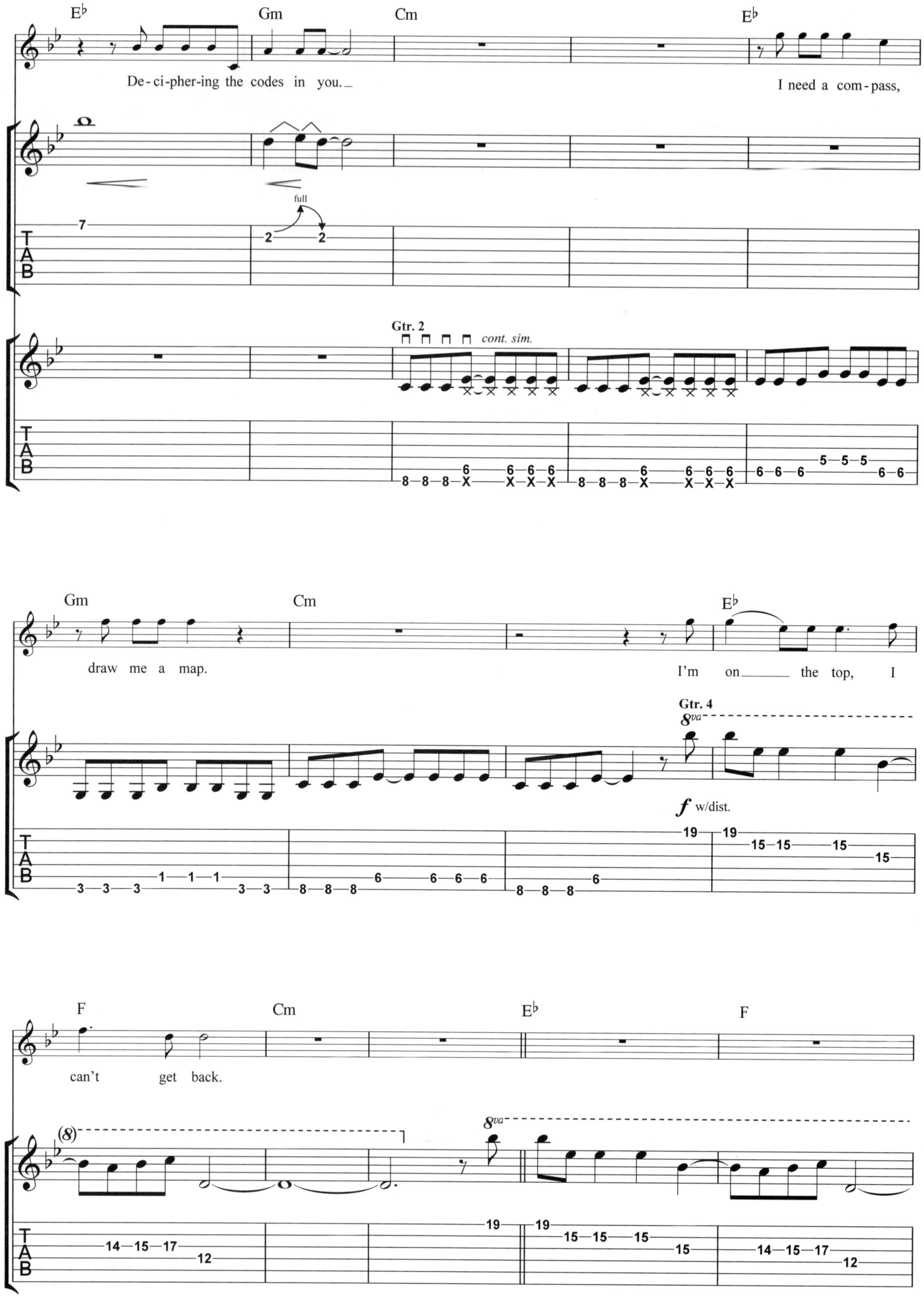
E♭ Gm Cm E♭
De-ci-pher-ing the codes in you.
I need a com-pass,
full
Gtr. 2
cont. sim.
Gm Cm E♭
draw me a map.
I'm on the top, I
Gtr. 4
8va
f w/dist.
F Cm E♭ F
can't get back.
(8)
8va

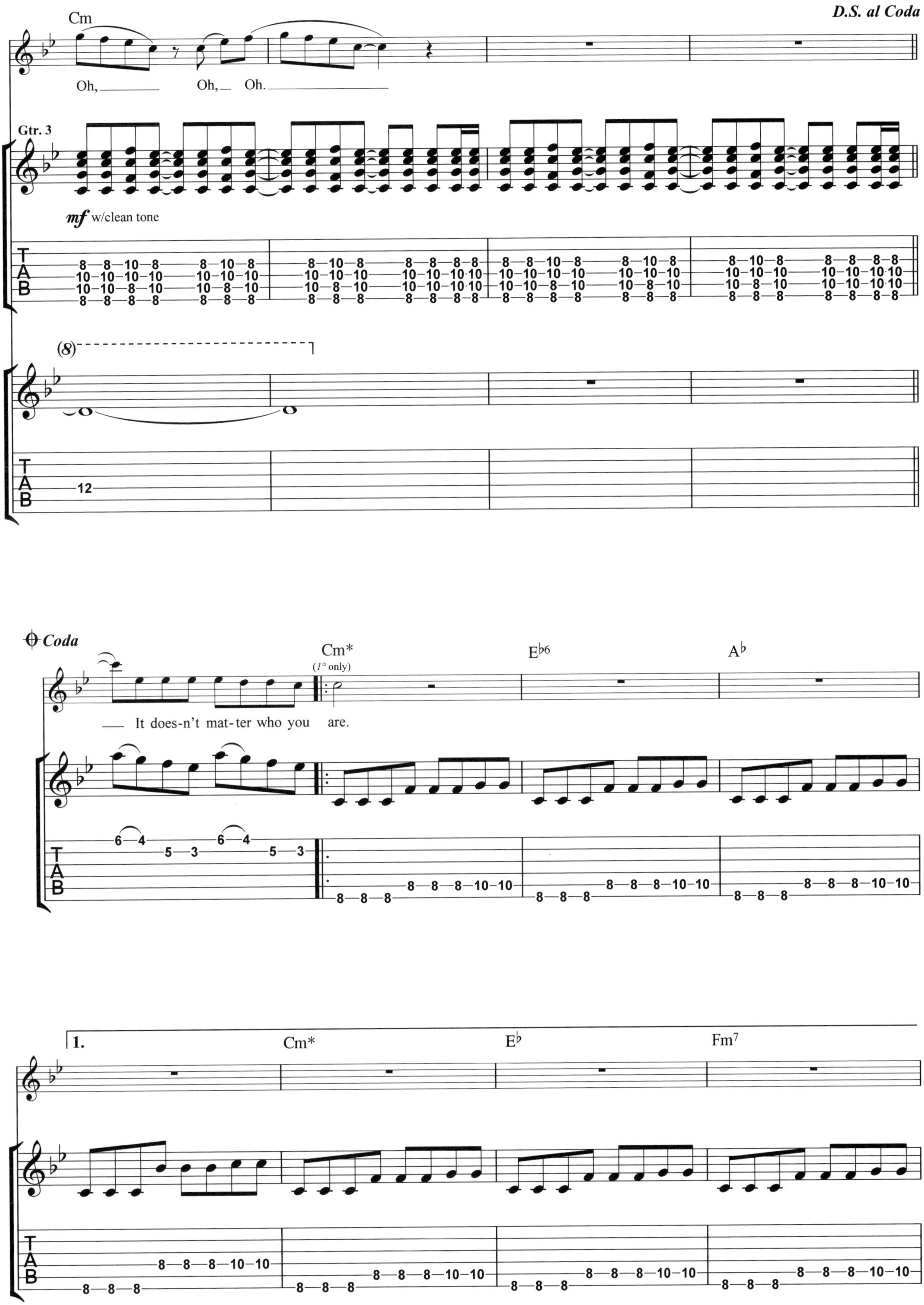
D.S. al Coda
Cm
Oh, Oh, Oh.
Gtr. 3
mf w/clean tone
(8)
Coda
Cm*
(1° only)
E♭6
A♭
It does-n't mat-ter who you are.
1.
Cm*
E♭
Fm7

2.
Chorus
B♭add9(11)
You just want
some - bo - dy
A♭
lis - ten - ing to what you say.
You just want
Fm7
some - bo - dy
B♭add9(11)
lis - ten - ing to what you say.
A♭
It does - n't mat - ter who
F7
you are.
It does - n't mat - ter who

F7
(1° only)
1.
you are.
Gtr. 1
fade in
cont. sim.
2.
Fm7
A♭
Is there an - y - bo - dy out there who is
Gtr. 6 (acous.)
p
mf
* Use Thumb on 6
Fm7
Cm*
lost and hurt, and lone - ly too? Are they bleed - ing all your co -

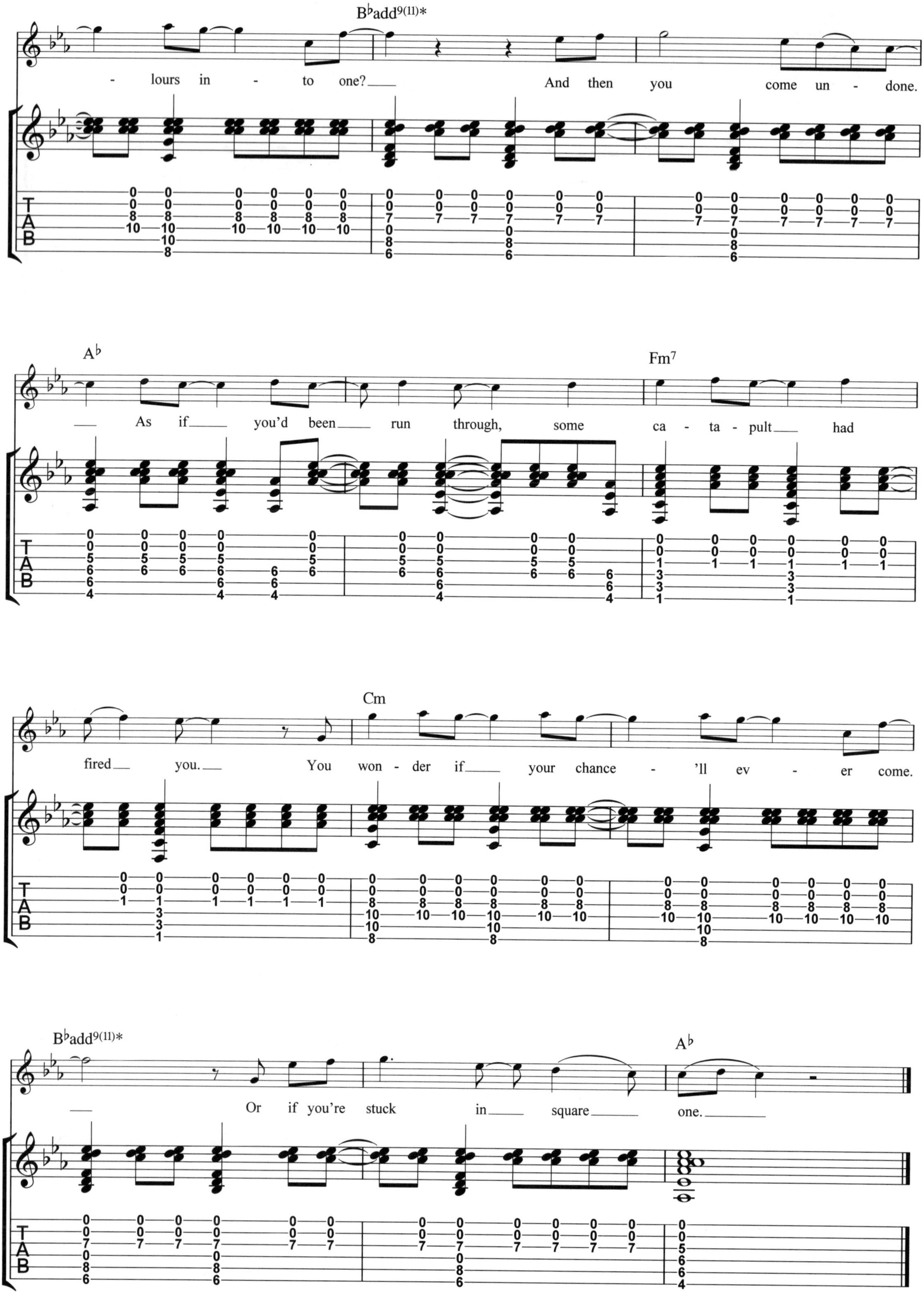
B♭add9(11)*
-lours in-to one? And then you come un-done.
A♭
As if you'd been run through, some
Fm7
ca-ta-pult had
fired you. You
Cm
won-der if your chance-'ll ev-er come.
B♭add9(11)*
Or if you're stuck in square
A♭
one.
TAB

WHAT IF

Words & Music by Guy Berryman, Jon Buckland, Will Champion & Chris Martin

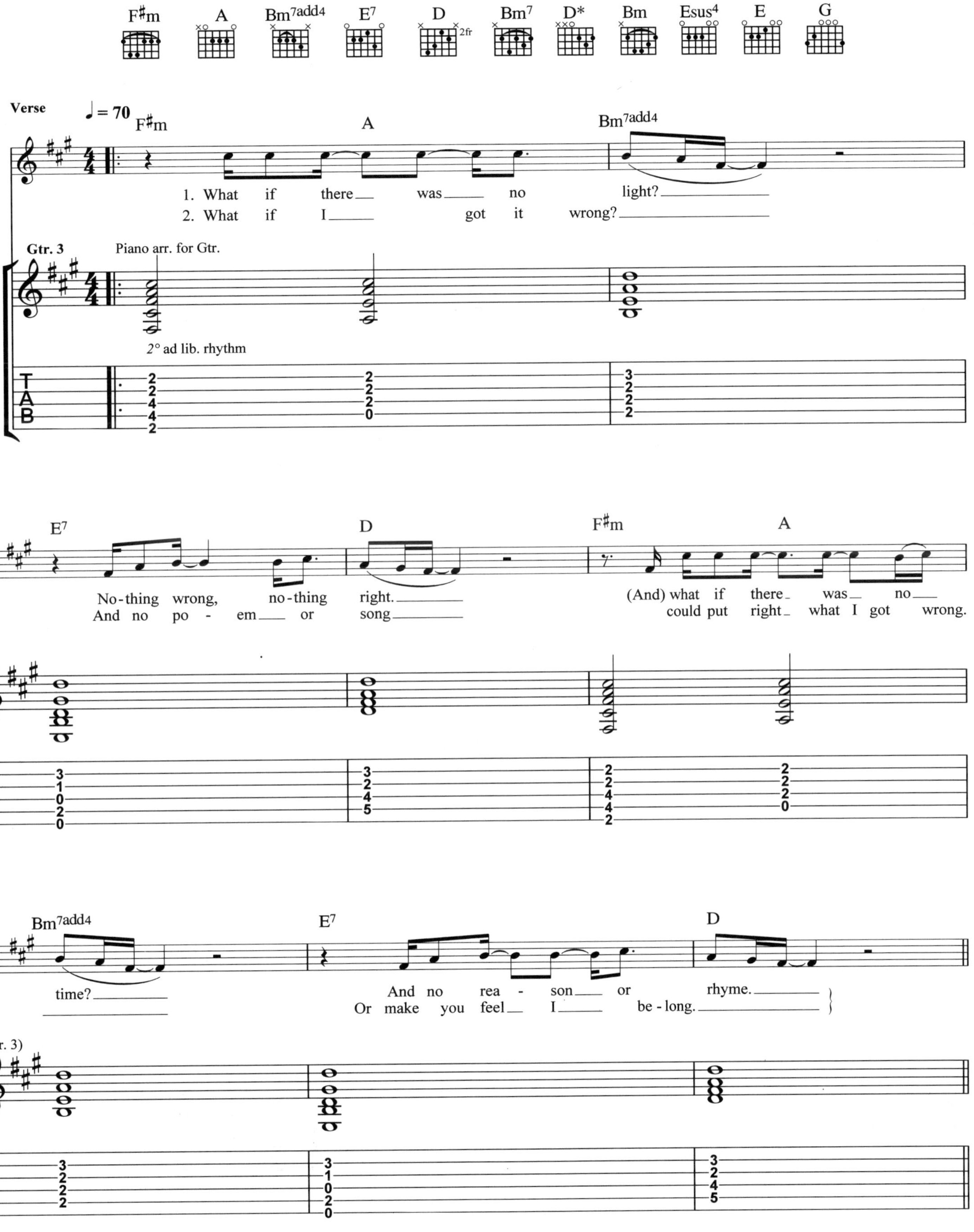

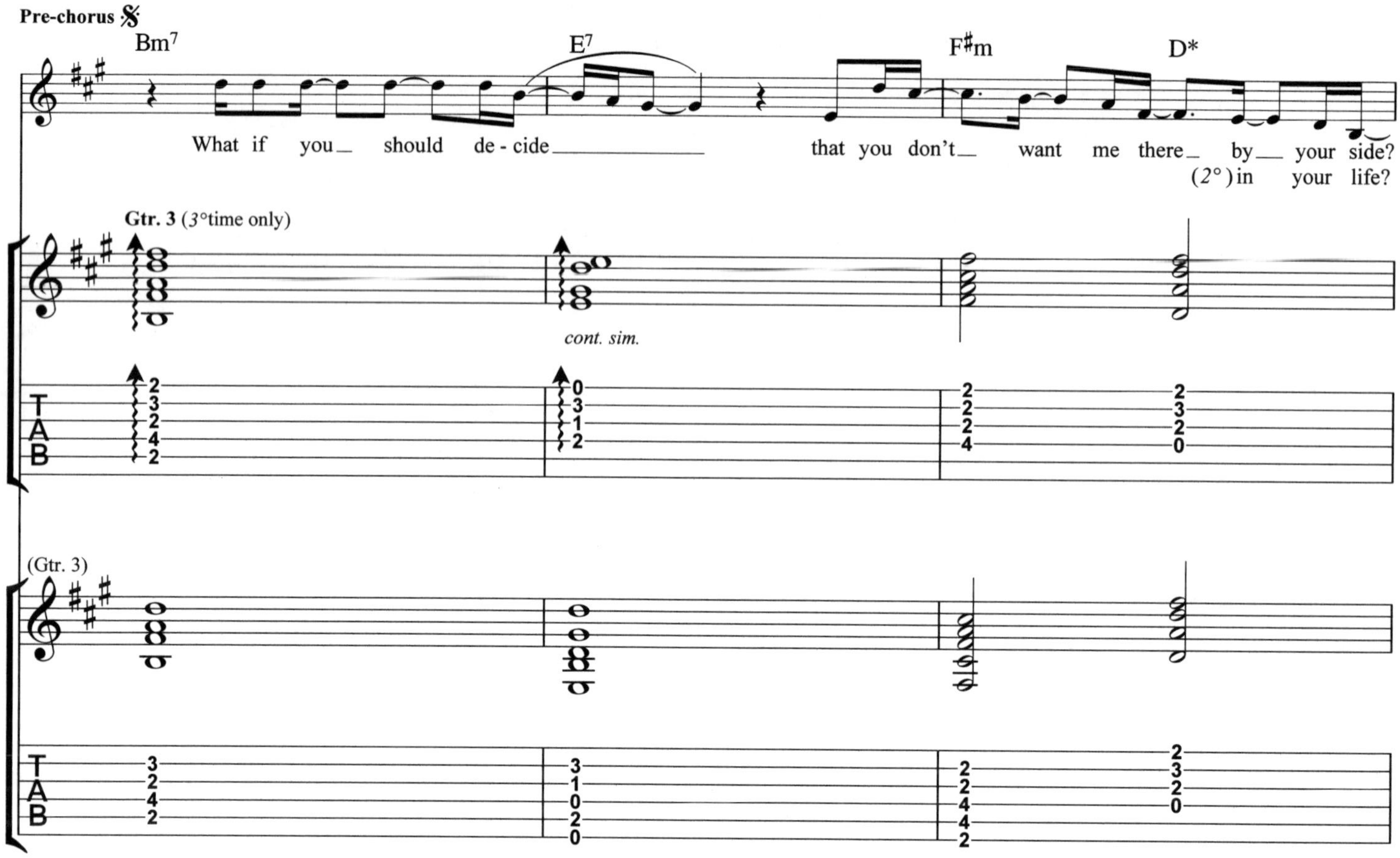
Pre-chorus
Bm7
E7
F#m
D*
What if you should de-cide that you don't want me there by your side?
(2°) in your life?
Gtr. 3 (3°time only)
cont. sim.
(Gtr. 3)
TAB

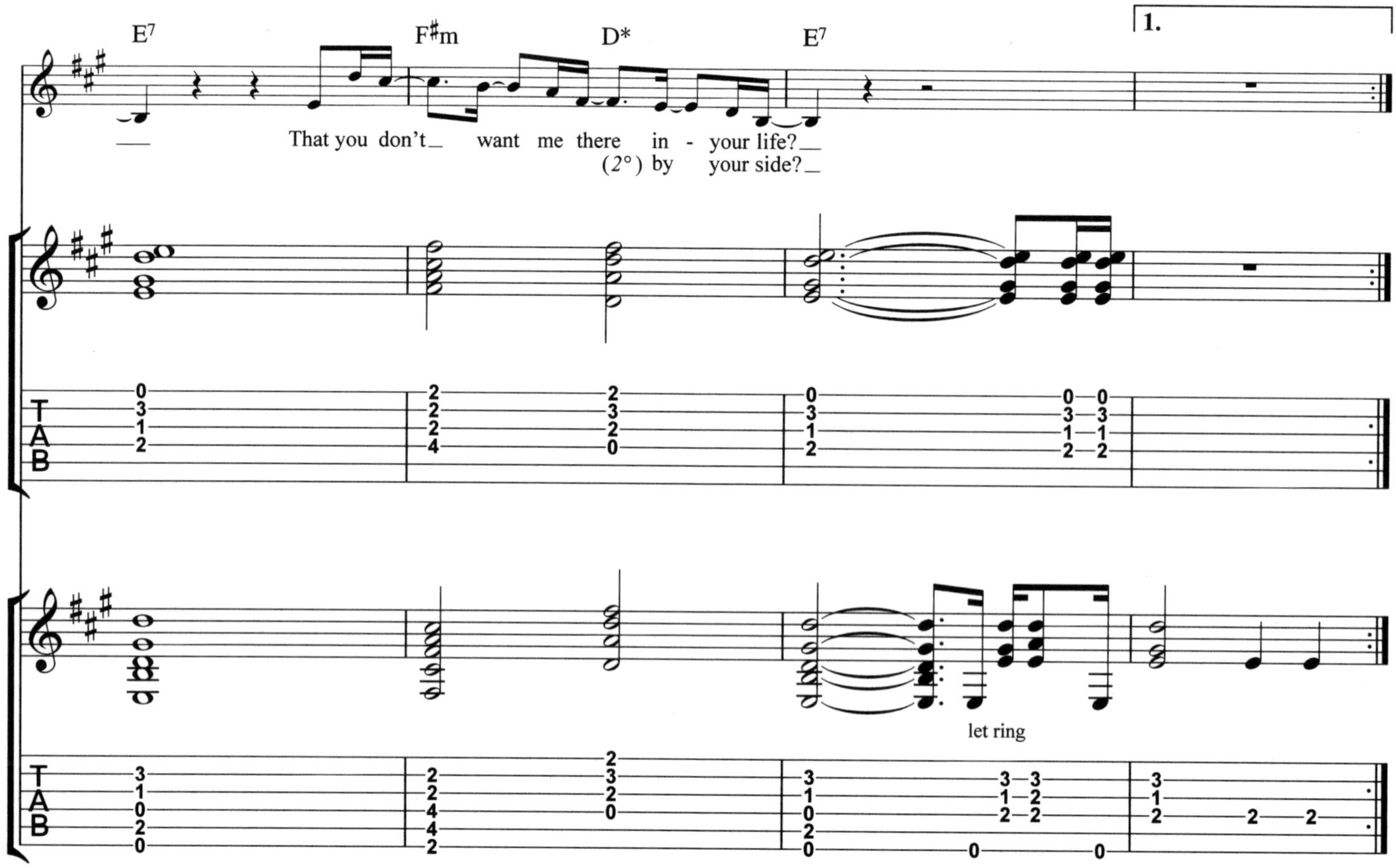
E7
F#m
D*
E7
1.
That you don't want me there in - your life?
(2°) by your side?
TAB
let ring

2, 3.
Chorus
D*
Bm
Gtr. 2 (acous.)
cont. sim.
Ooh, that's right.
Gtr. 1
mf w/dist.
F#m
Esus4
E
D*
Let's take a breath, jump ov - er the side.
Ooh, that's
(Gtr. 1)

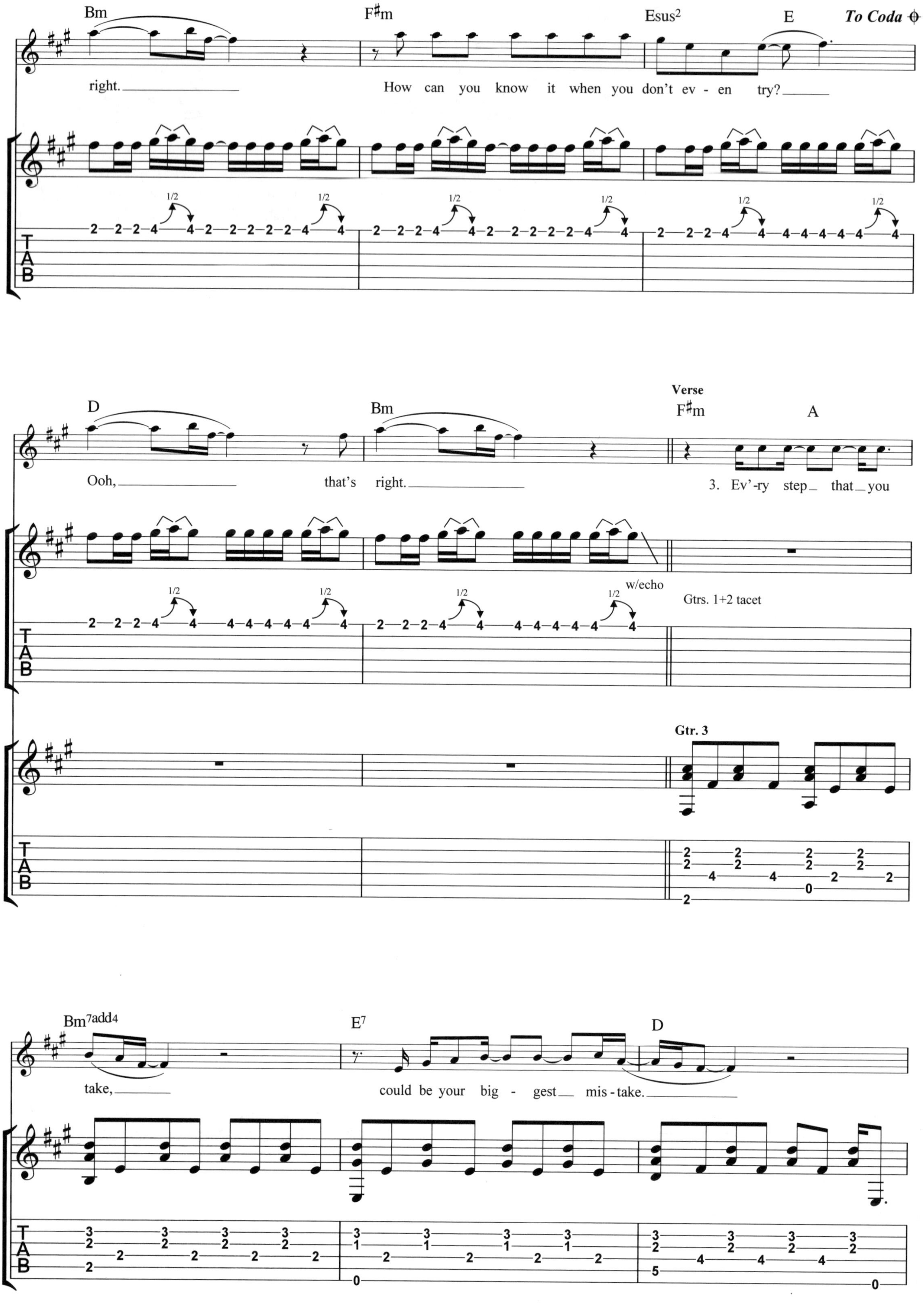
Bm
F♯m
Esus2
E
To Coda
right.
How can you know it when you don't ev - en try?
1/2
D
Bm
Verse
F♯m
A
Ooh,
that's right.
3. Ev'-ry step that you
w/echo
Gtrs. 1+2 tacet
Gtr. 3
Bm7add4
E7
D
take,
could be your big - gest mis - take.

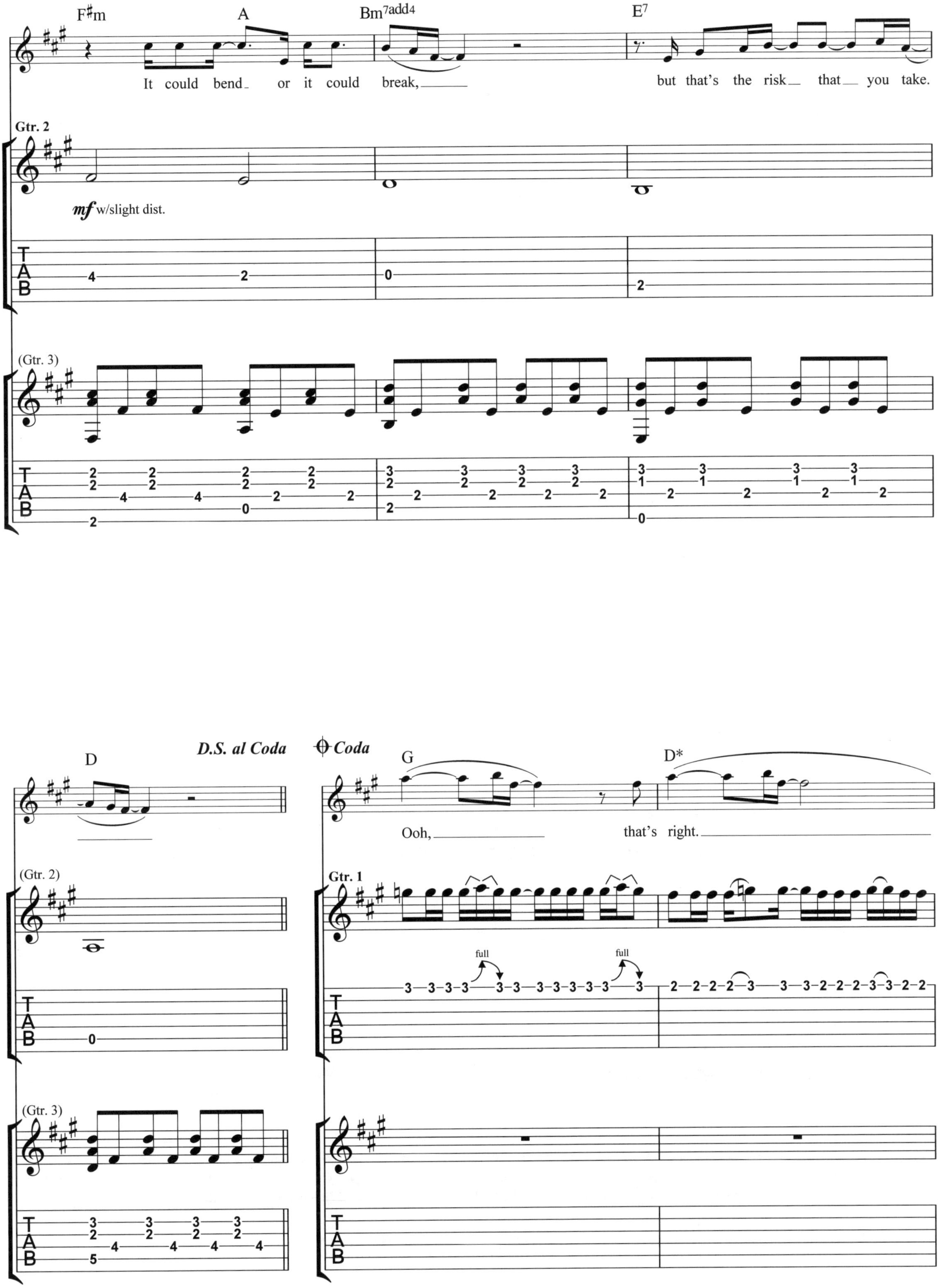
F♯m A Bm7add4 E7
It could bend or it could break, but that's the risk that you take.
Gtr. 2
mf w/slight dist.
(Gtr. 3)
D
D.S. al Coda
Coda
G D*
Ooh, that's right.
(Gtr. 2)
Gtr. 1
full
full
(Gtr. 3)

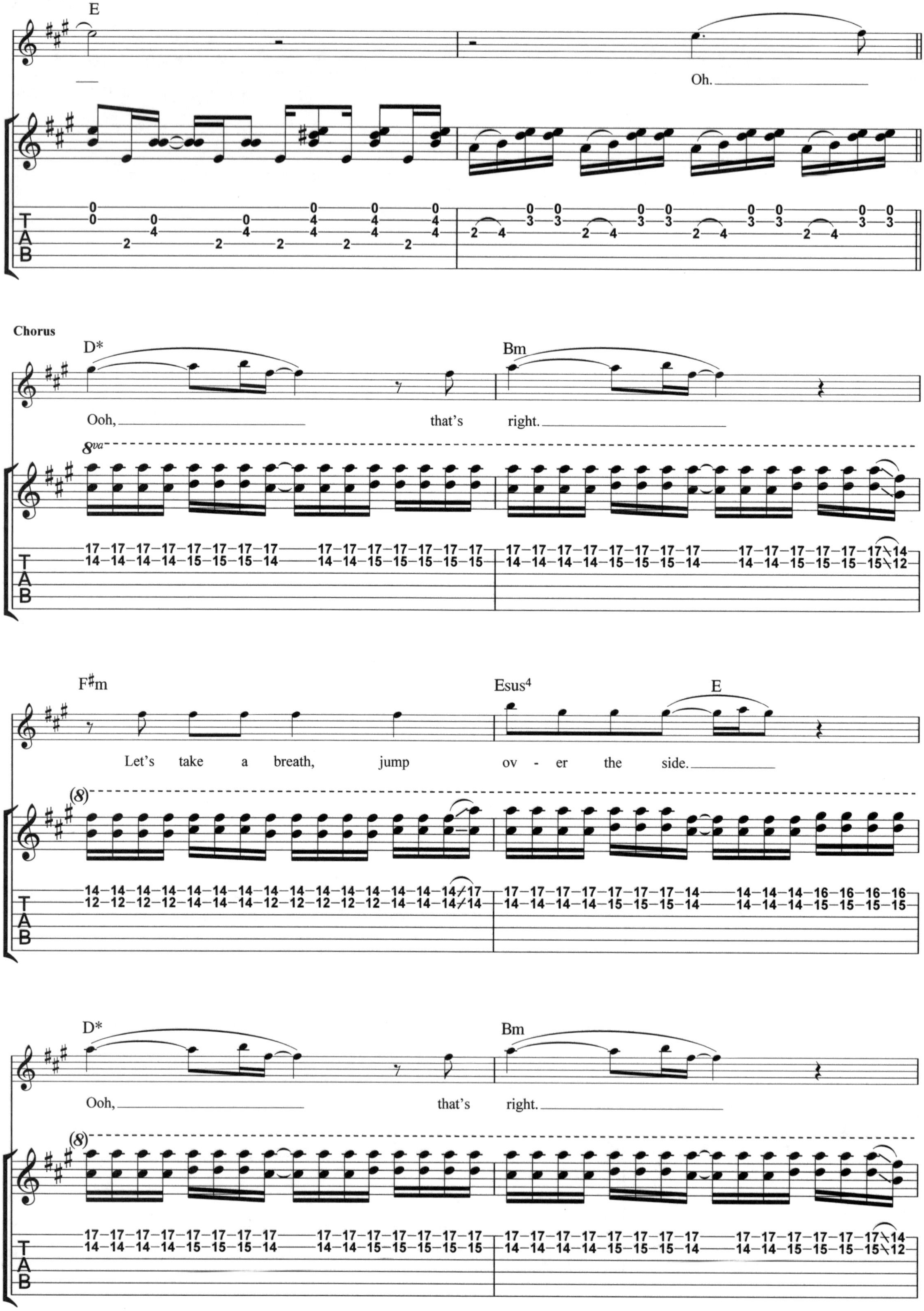
E
Oh.
Chorus
D*
Bm
Ooh, that's right.
8va
F#m
Esus4
E
Let's take a breath, jump ov - er the side.
(8)
D*
Bm
Ooh, that's right.
(8)
T
A
B

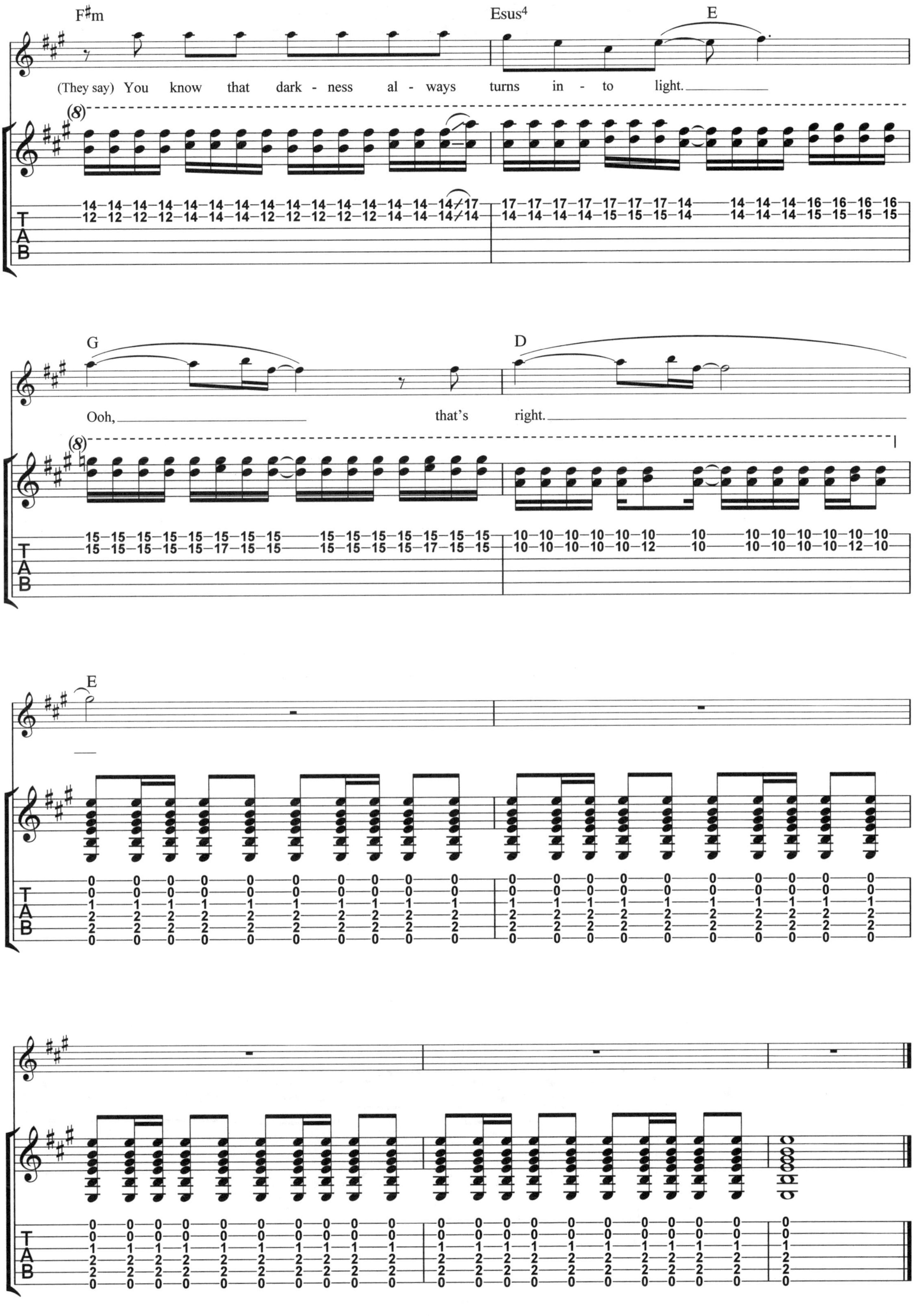
F♯m
Esus4
E
(They say) You know that dark - ness al - ways turns in - to light.
G
D
Ooh, that's right.
E

WHITE SHADOWS

Words & Music by Guy Berryman, Jon Buckland, Will Champion & Chris Martin

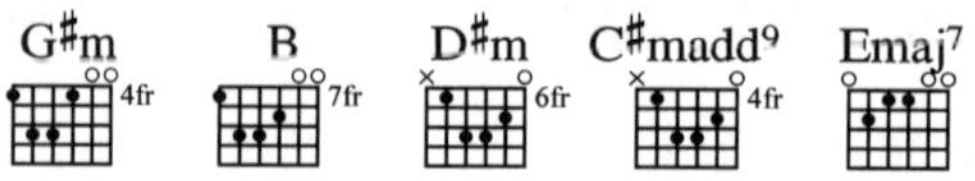

Gtr. 3 (acous.)	
6 = E	3 = G
5 = A	2 = B
4 = D	1 = D#

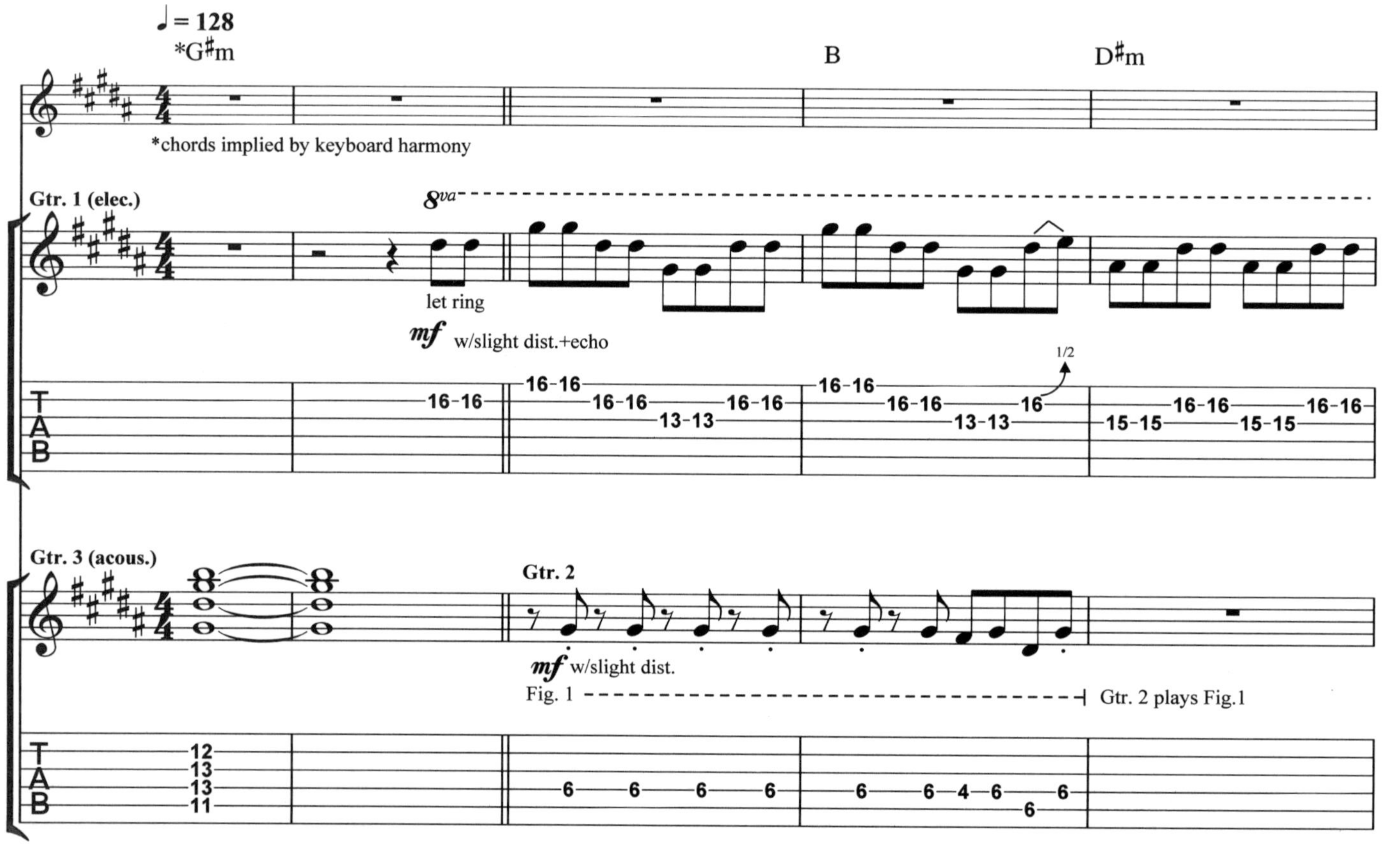

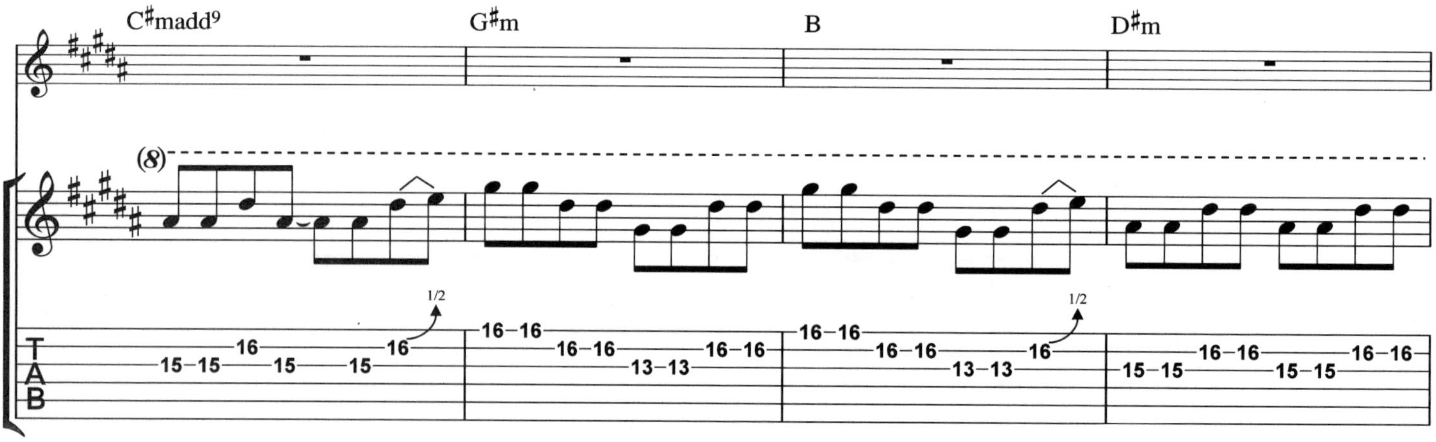

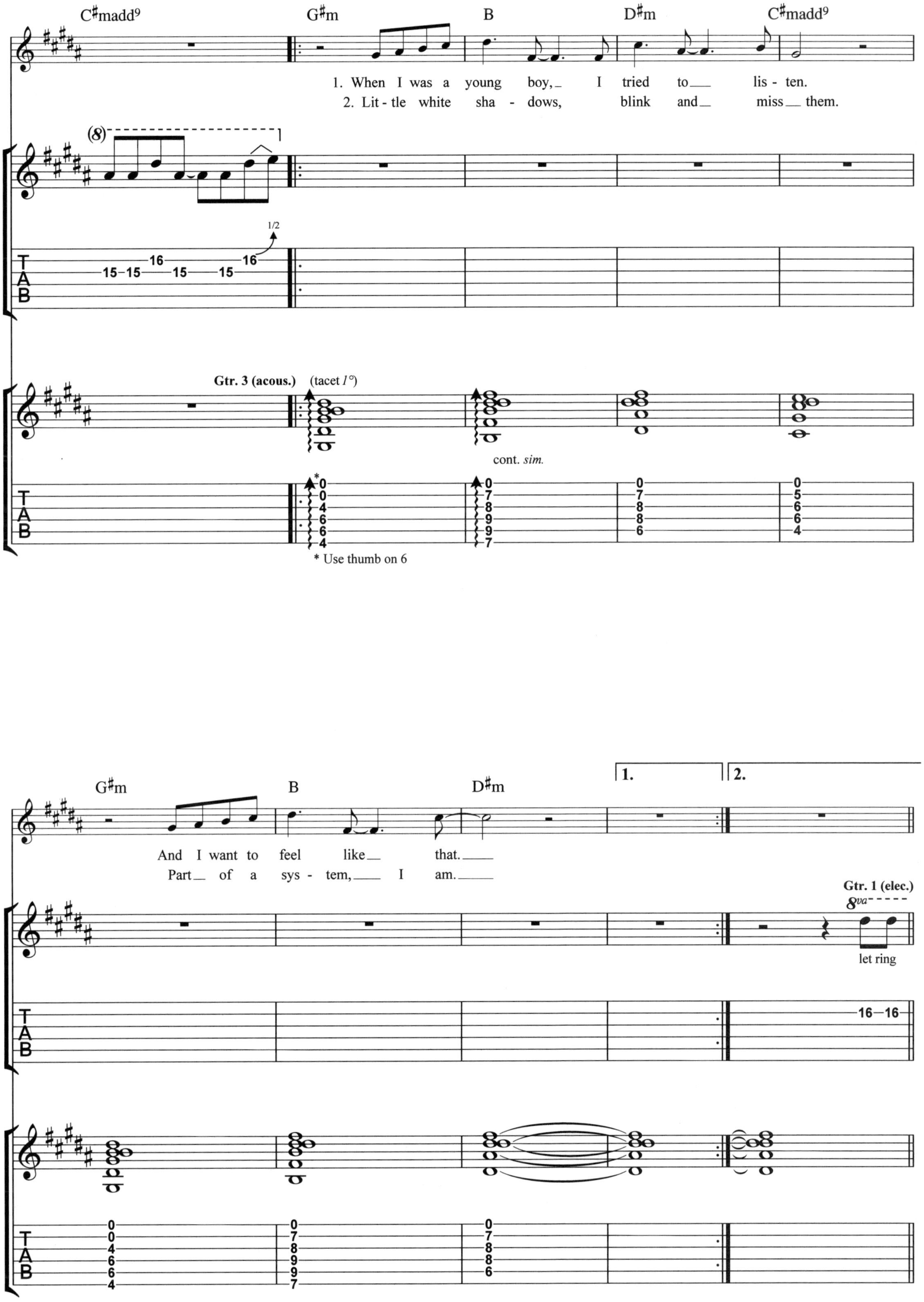
C♯madd9
G♯m
B
D♯m
C♯madd9
1. When I was a young boy, I tried to lis - ten.
2. Lit - tle white sha - dows, blink and miss them.
(8)
1/2
Gtr. 3 (acous.)
(tacet 1°)
cont. sim.
* Use thumb on 6
G♯m
B
D♯m
1.
2.
And I want to feel like that.
Part of a sys - tem, I am.
Gtr. 1 (elec.)
8va
let ring

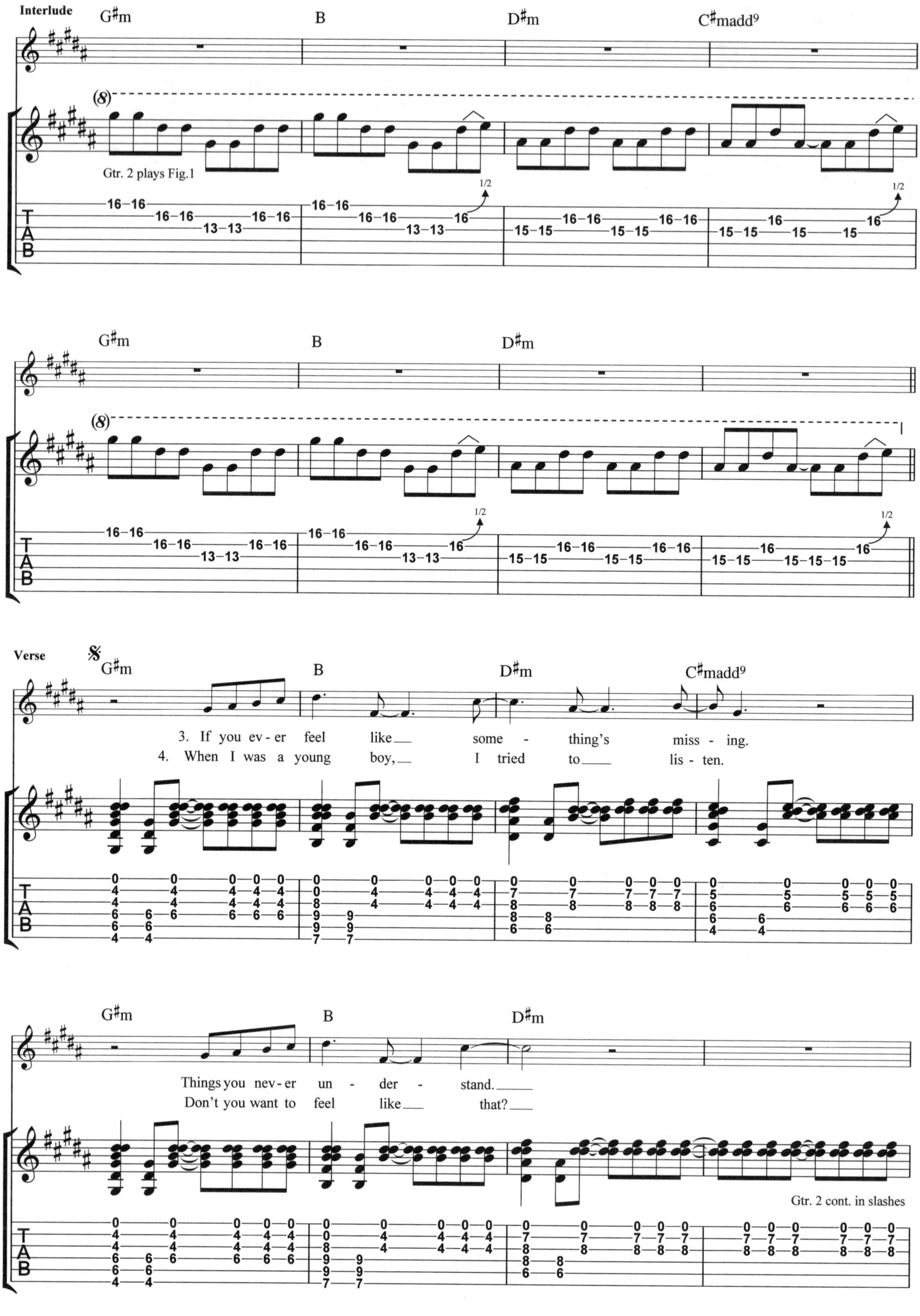
Interlude
G♯m
B
D♯m
C♯madd9
Gtr. 2 plays Fig.1
Verse
3. If you ev - er feel like some - thing's miss - ing.
4. When I was a young boy, I tried to lis - ten.
Things you nev - er un - der - stand.
Don't you want to feel like that?
Gtr. 2 cont. in slashes

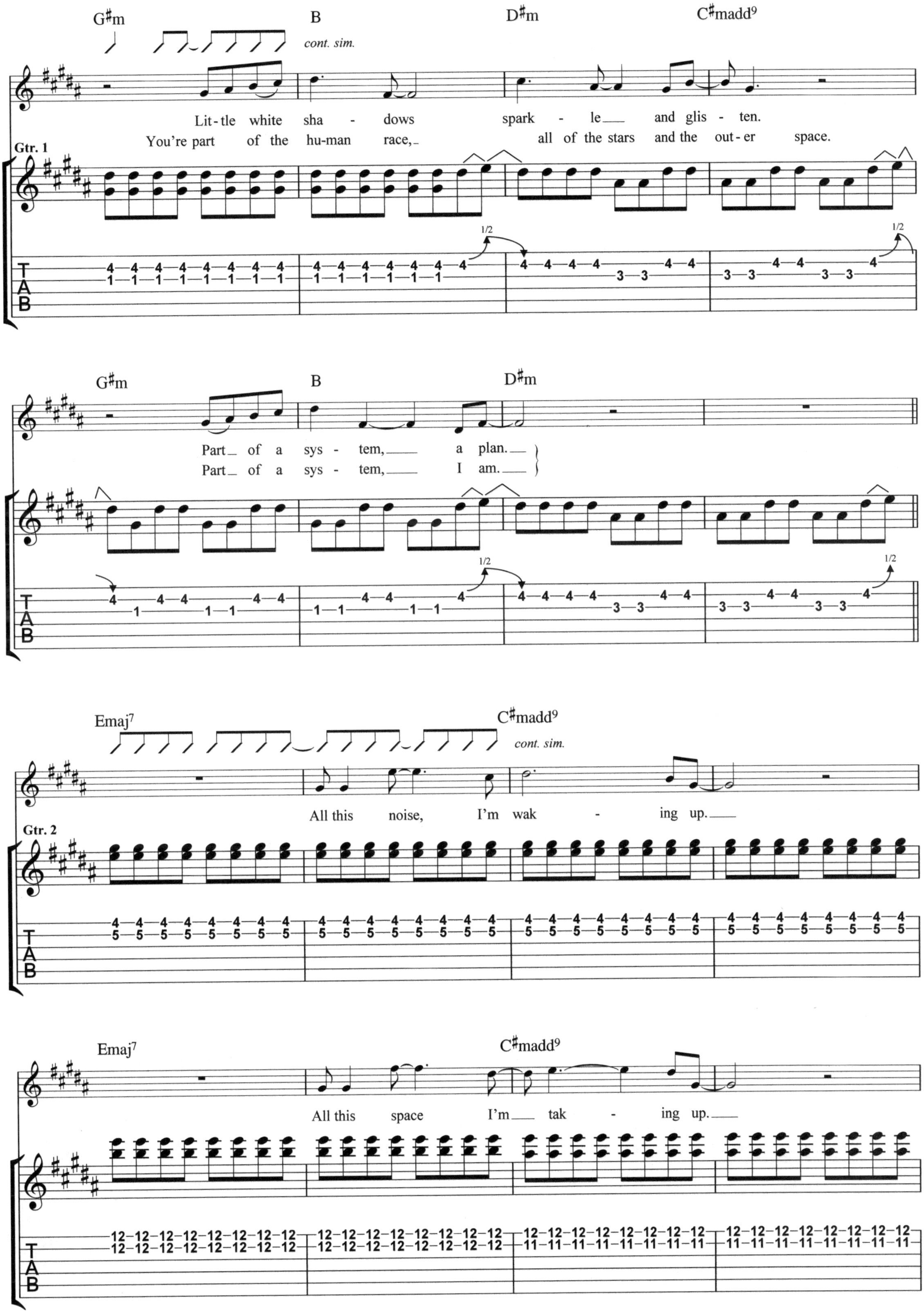
G♯m B D♯m C♯madd9
cont. sim.
Lit-tle white sha - dows spark - le and glis - ten.
You're part of the hu-man race, all of the stars and the out-er space.
Gtr. 1
G♯m B D♯m
Part of a sys - tem, a plan.
Part of a sys - tem, I am.
Emaj7 C♯madd9
cont. sim.
All this noise, I'm wak - ing up.
Gtr. 2
Emaj7 C♯madd9
All this space I'm tak - ing up.

Emaj7
C♯madd9
All this sound is break - ing up.
I can-not hear, you're break - ing up.
Emaj7
C♯madd9
Oh, Oh.
G♯m
Emaj7
B
May - be you'll get what you want - ed,
may - be you'll stum - ble up -
May - be you'll know when you've seen it,
may - be if you say it you'll
8va
D♯m
G♯m
Emaj7
B
- on it.
Ev' - ry-thing you ev - er want - ed, in a per - ma - nent state.
mean it.
And when you find it you'll keep it, in a per - ma - nent state,
May - be you'll find you're com - plet - ed
(8)

1, 3.
D♯m
2, 4.
D♯m
To Coda
Interlude
G♯m
a per - ma - nent state.
Gtr. 2 plays Fig. 1
Gtr. 3 tacet
B
D♯m
C♯madd9
G♯m
B
D♯m
D.S. al Coda
Coda
G♯m
Emaj7
state.
Keyboards arr. for Gtr. 3

B
D♯m
G♯m
Emaj7
Swim out on a sea of fac - es, the tide of the
See it in the new sun - rise, and see it break - ing on
B
hu - man rac - es. Oh, an an - swer now, is what I
your ho - ri - zon. Oh, come on love, stay with
D♯m
G♯m
need.
me.
T
A
B

FIX YOU

Words & Music by Guy Berryman, Jon Buckland, Will Champion & Chris Martin

Gtrs. 1+2
6 = E♭ 3 = G♭
5 = A♭ 2 = B♭
4 = D♭ 1 = E♭

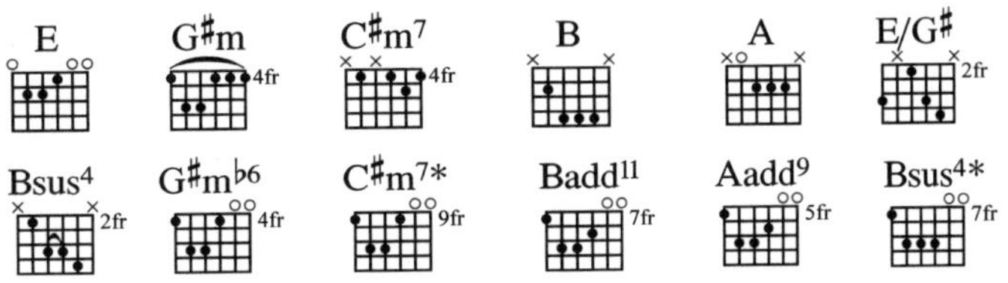

E G#m 1. C#m7 B 2. C#m7 B Chorus A E/G# Bsus4 B
verse.
worse.
2. And the tears
Lights will guide you home,
A E/G# Bsus4 B A E/G# Bsus4 B
and ig - nite your bones. And I will try to fix you.
E E/G# Bsus4 B E E/G# Bsus4 B
3. High
Verse
E G#mb6 C#m7* Badd11
up a - bove and down be - low. You're
Gtr. 1 (acous.)
* Use thumb on 6

E G#m♭6 C#m7* Badd11 E G#m♭6
too in love to let it go.
But if you nev-er try, you'll nev-er know
C#m7* Badd11 E G#m♭6
just what you're worth.
C#m7* Badd11
Chorus
Aadd9 G#m♭6
Lights will
Bsus4* Badd11 Aadd9 G#m♭6
guide you home, and ig -

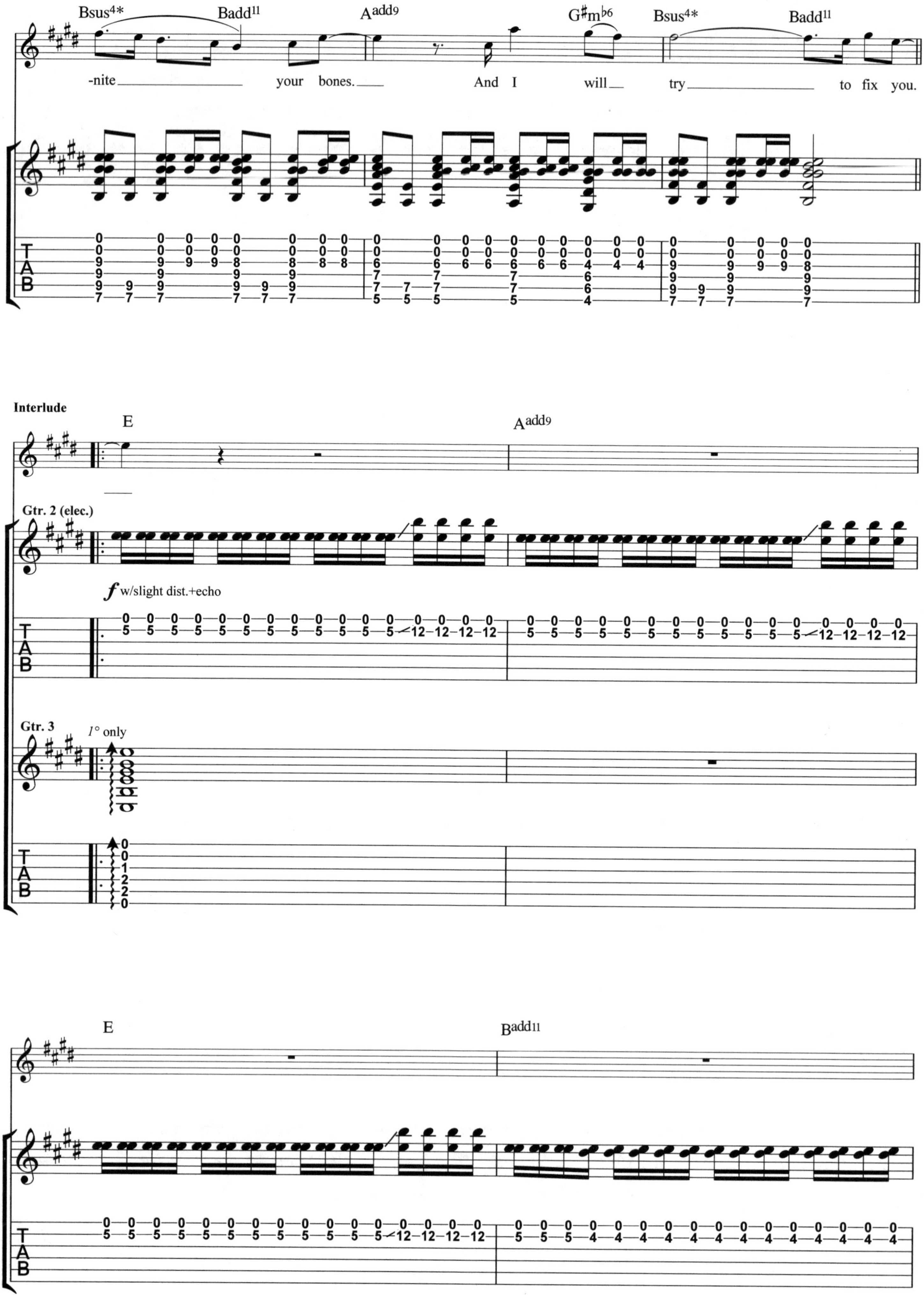
Bsus4* Badd11 Aadd9 G#m♭6 Bsus4* Badd11
-nite your bones. And I will try to fix you.
Interlude
E Aadd9
Gtr. 2 (elec.)
f w/slight dist.+echo
Gtr. 3
1° only
E Badd11

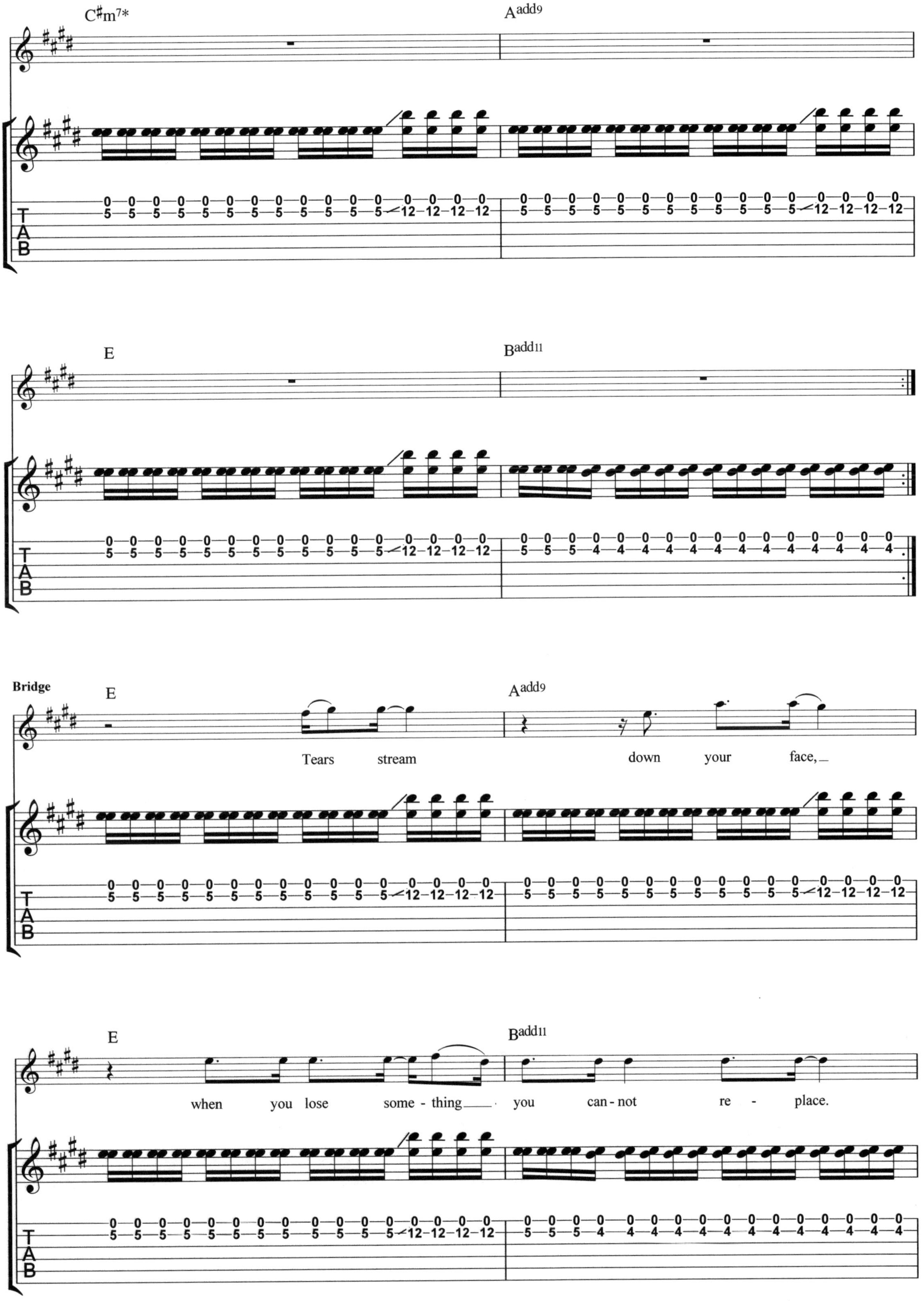
C#m7*
Aadd9
E
Badd11
Bridge
E
Aadd9
Tears stream down your face, _
E
Badd11
when you lose some - thing ___ you can - not re - place.
TAB

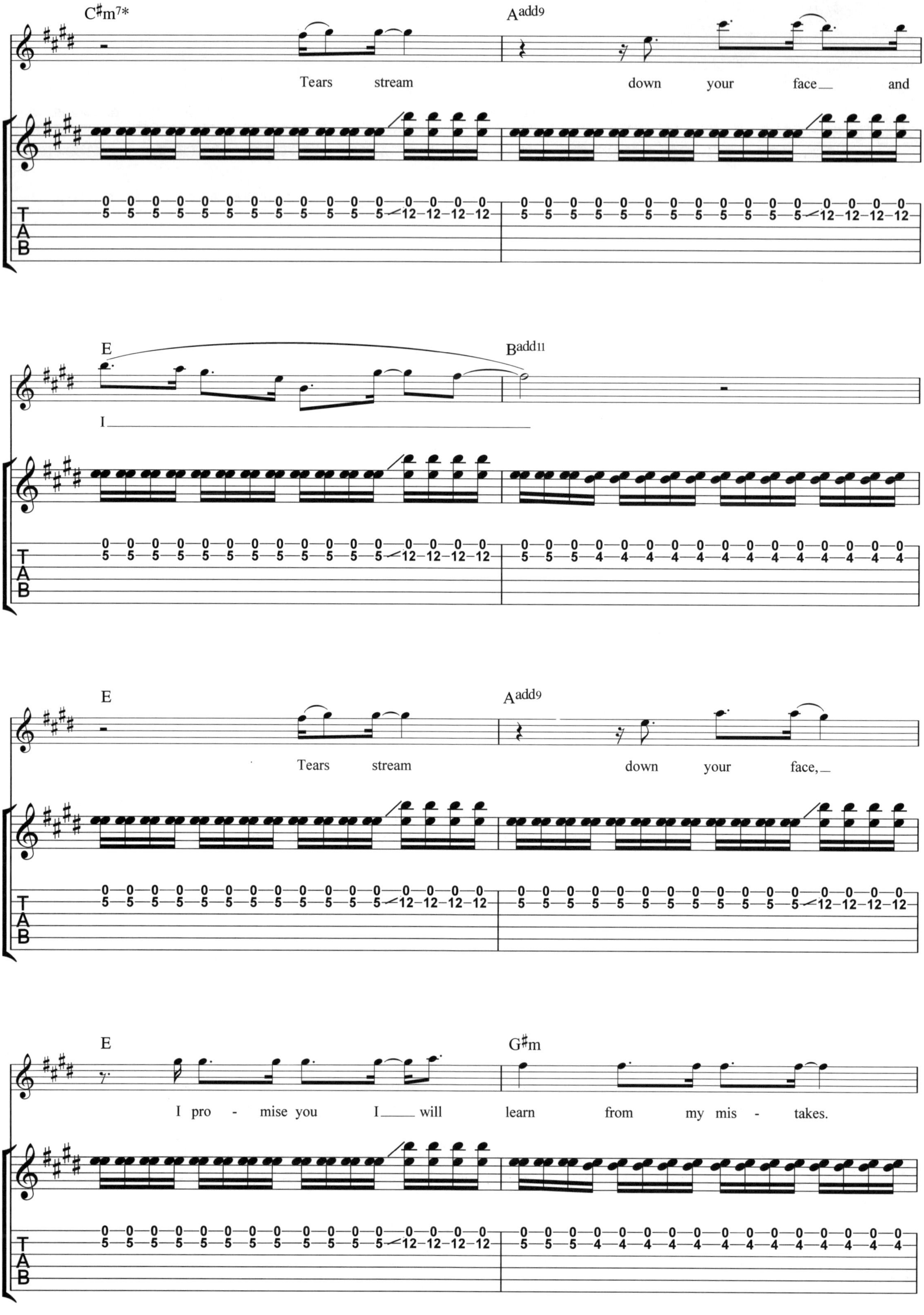
C#m7*
Aadd9
Tears stream down your face and
E
Badd11
I
E
Aadd9
Tears stream down your face,
E
G#m
I pro - mise you I will learn from my mis - takes.

C♯m7*
Aadd9
Tears stream down your face and
E
Badd11
I
Outro
A E/G♯ Bsus4 B A E/G♯ Bsus4 B
Lights will guide you home, and ig - nite your bones.
Gtr. 3
Piano arr. for Gtr.
A E/G♯ Bsus4 B E
And I will try to fix you.

TALK

Words & Music by Guy Berryman, Jon Buckland, Will Champion,
Chris Martin, Karl Bartos, Ralf Huetter & Emil Schult

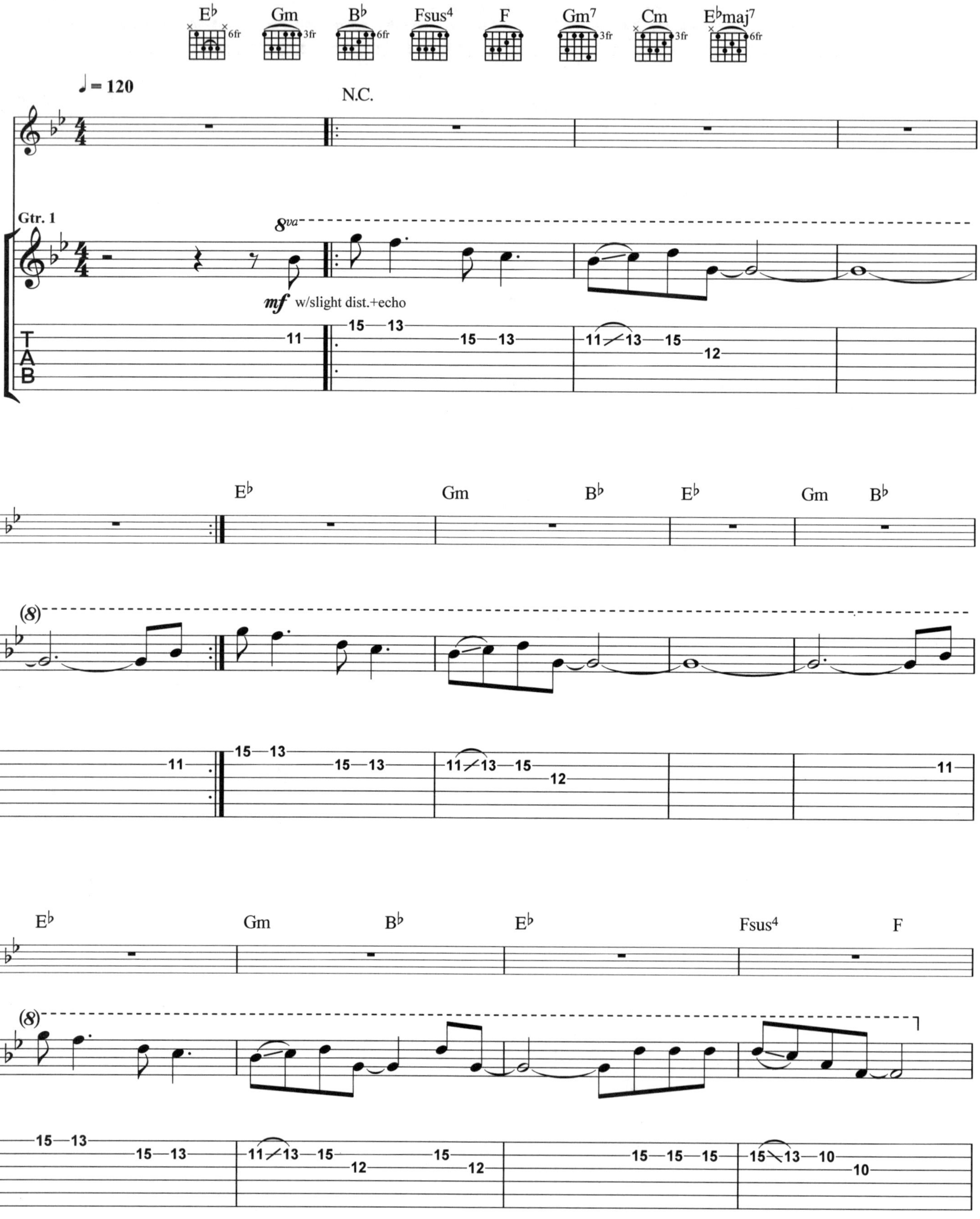

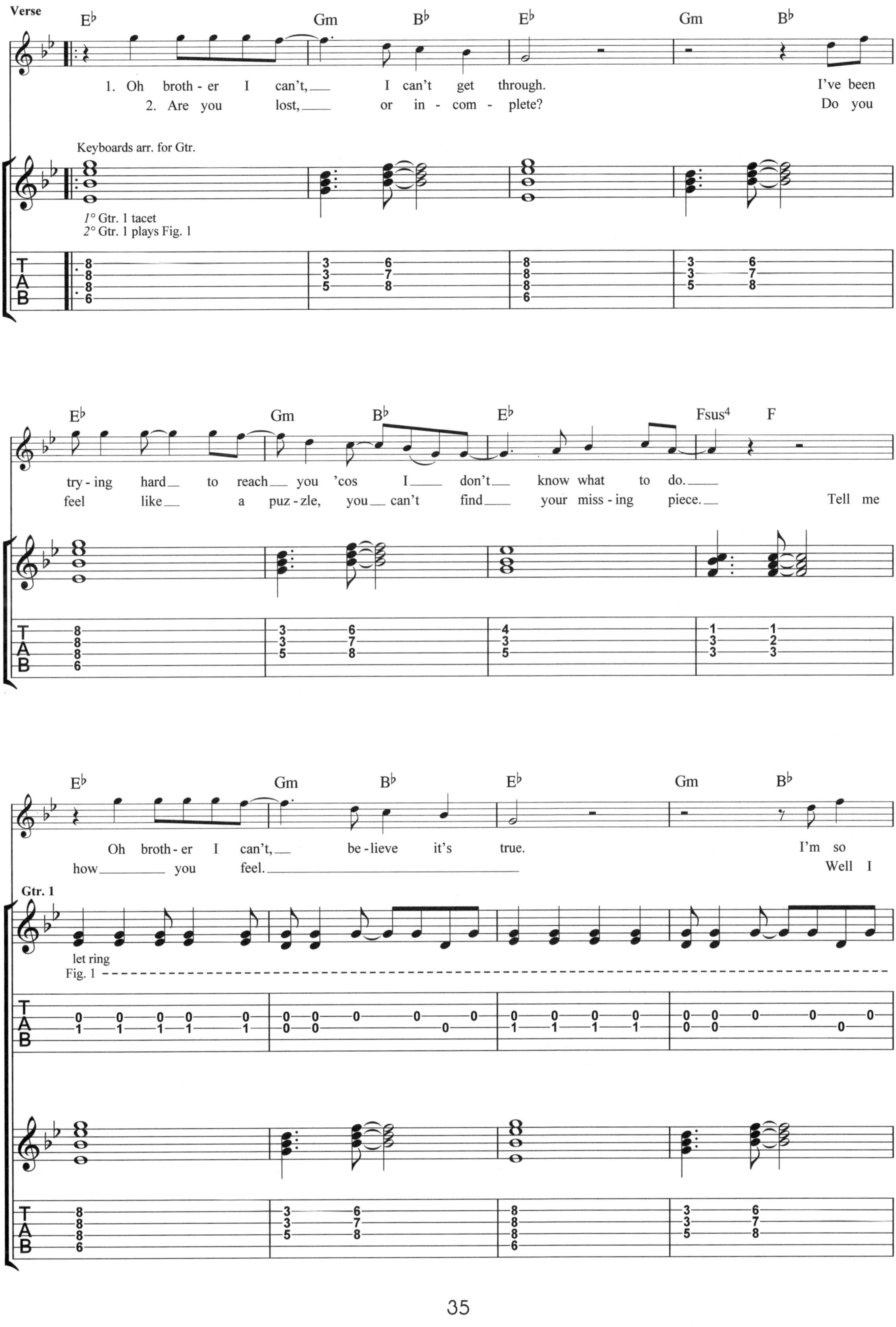
Verse
E♭ Gm B♭ E♭ Gm B♭
1. Oh broth - er I can't, I can't get through. I've been
2. Are you lost, or in - com - plete? Do you
Keyboards arr. for Gtr.
1° Gtr. 1 tacet
2° Gtr. 1 plays Fig. 1
E♭ Gm B♭ E♭ Fsus4 F
try - ing hard to reach you 'cos I don't know what to do.
feel like a puz - zle, you can't find your miss - ing piece. Tell me
E♭ Gm B♭ E♭ Gm B♭
Oh broth - er I can't, be - lieve it's true. I'm so
how you feel. Well I
Gtr. 1
let ring
Fig. 1

E♭ Gm B♭ E♭ Fsus4 F
scared a-bout the fu - ture and I want to talk to you. Oh, I want
feel like they're talk - ing in a lan - guage I don't speak. And they're talk
E♭ Fsus4 F
Pre-chorus
Gm
to talk to you.
- ing it to me.
You could
E♭ Gm B♭ E♭ Gm B♭ E♭
take a pic-ture of some-thing you see.
In the fu-ture,
Gtr. 1
8va
TAB

Gm Bb Eb Gm Bb Eb
where will I be? You could climb a lad-der
Gm Bb Eb Gm Bb Eb
up to the sun. Or write a song no-
Gm Bb Eb 1. Fsus4 F
-bo-dy had sung, or do some-thing that's nev-er been done.
Gm7 2. Fsus4 F
nev-er been done. Do
8va

E♭
Fsus4
F
Interlude
Gm7
some-thing that's nev - er been done.
(8)
Bridge
Gtr. 3
Cm
Keyboards arr. for Gtr.
E♭
Gm
F
Cm
E♭
Gm
Gtr. 1
F
Cm
E♭
Gm
F
let ring
cont. sim.
Gtr. solo
E♭
Gm
B♭
E♭
Gm
B♭
Gtr. 2 dbls w/dist.
E♭
Gm
B♭
E♭
F
So you

Chorus
E♭ Gm7 B♭ E♭ Gm7 B♭
don't know where you're go - ing and you want to talk.
an - y - one who'll lis - ten, but you feel ig - nored.
You
And
8va
Gtr. 2 tacet
1.
E♭ Gm7 B♭ E♭ Gm7 B♭
feel like you're go - ing where you've been be - fore.
You'll tell
2.
E♭ Gm7 B♭ E♭
no-thing's real - ly mak - ing an - y sense at all.
Let's talk, let's
F E♭maj7 F Gm
talk. Let's talk, let's talk.

X&Y

Words & Music by Guy Berryman, Jon Buckland, Will Champion & Chris Martin

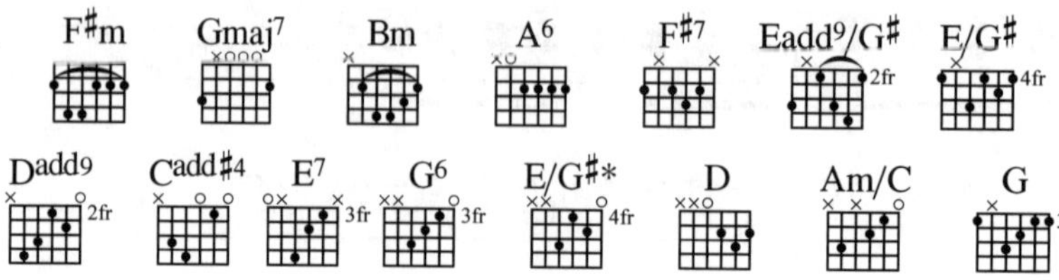

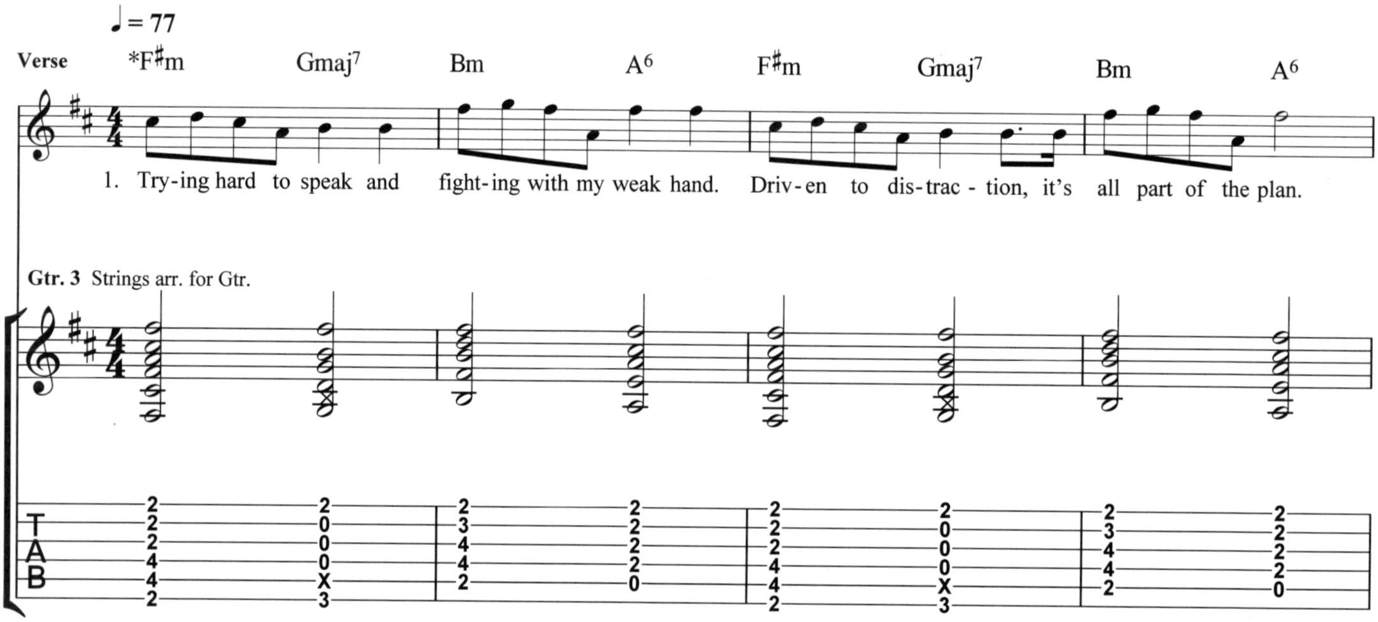

* chords implied by harmony

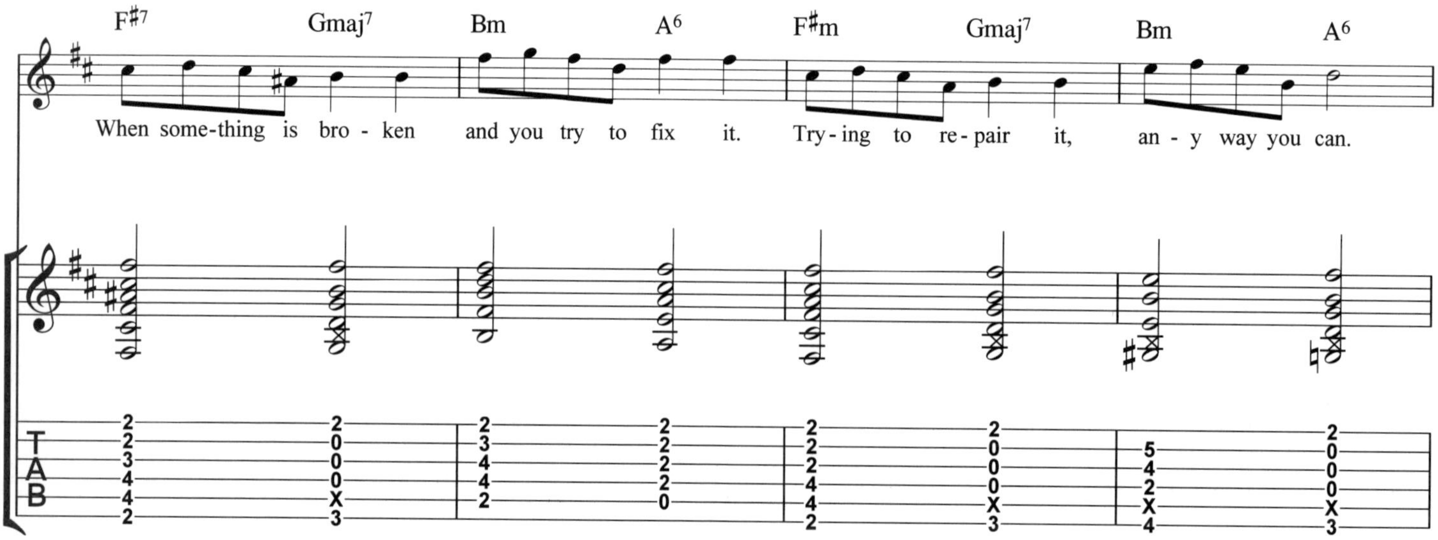

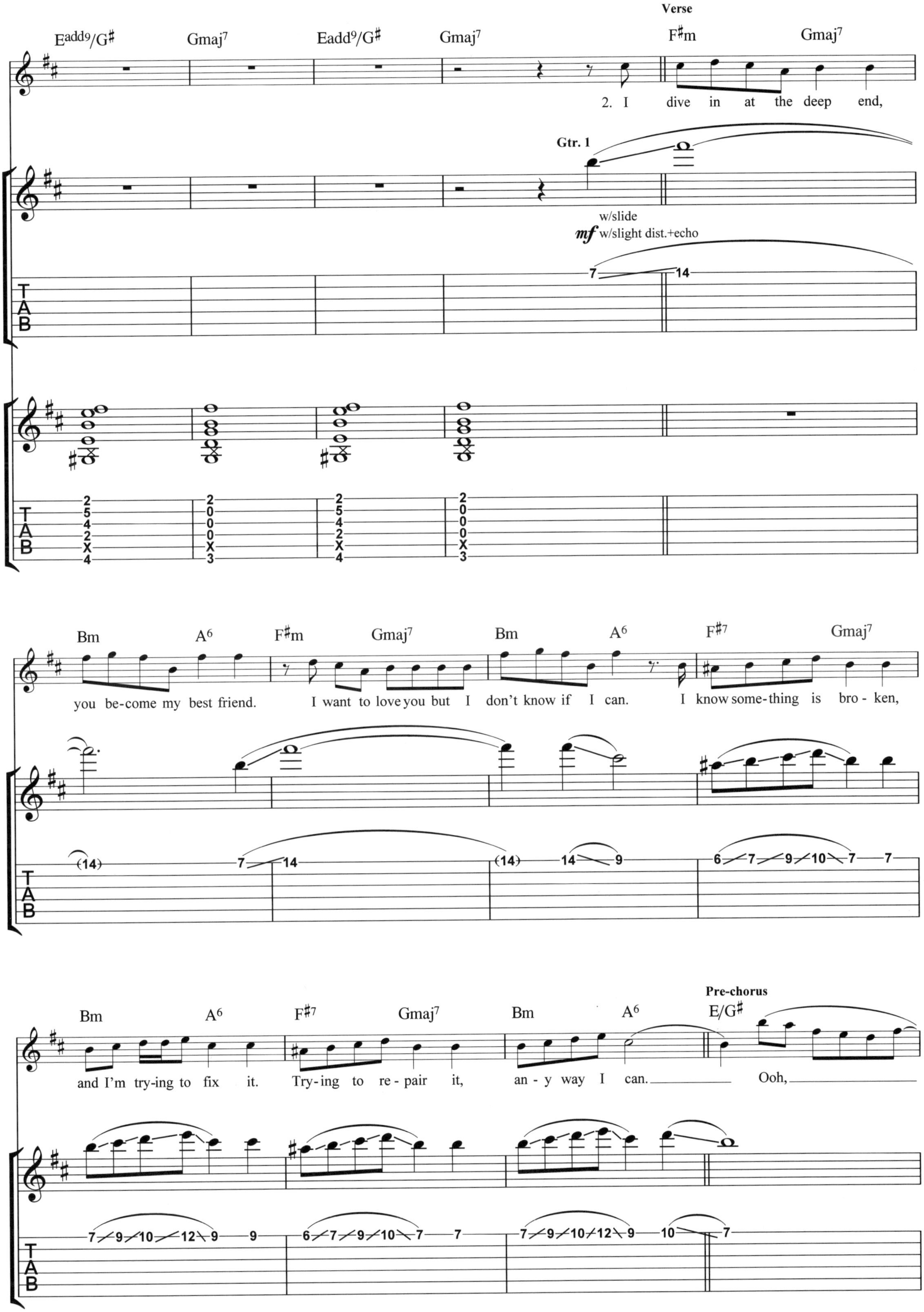
Verse
Eadd9/G♯ Gmaj7 Eadd9/G♯ Gmaj7 F♯m Gmaj7
2. I dive in at the deep end,
Gtr. 1
w/slide
mf w/slight dist.+echo
Bm A6 F♯m Gmaj7 Bm A6 F♯7 Gmaj7
you be-come my best friend. I want to love you but I don't know if I can. I know some-thing is bro-ken,
Pre-chorus
Bm A6 F♯7 Gmaj7 Bm A6 E/G♯
and I'm try-ing to fix it. Try-ing to re-pair it, an-y way I can. Ooh,

Gmaj7
E/G♯
Gmaj7
E/G♯
Gmaj7
E/G♯
Ooh.
Ooh,
Ooh.
Gtr. 2
w/slide
mf w/slight dist.
Gmaj7
𝄋 Chorus
Dadd9
Cadd♯4
E7
You and me are float - ing on a ti - dal wave,
Gtr. 3
let ring
mf clean tone
Dadd9
Cadd♯4
E7
to-geth - er. You and me are drift - ing in - to out - er space,

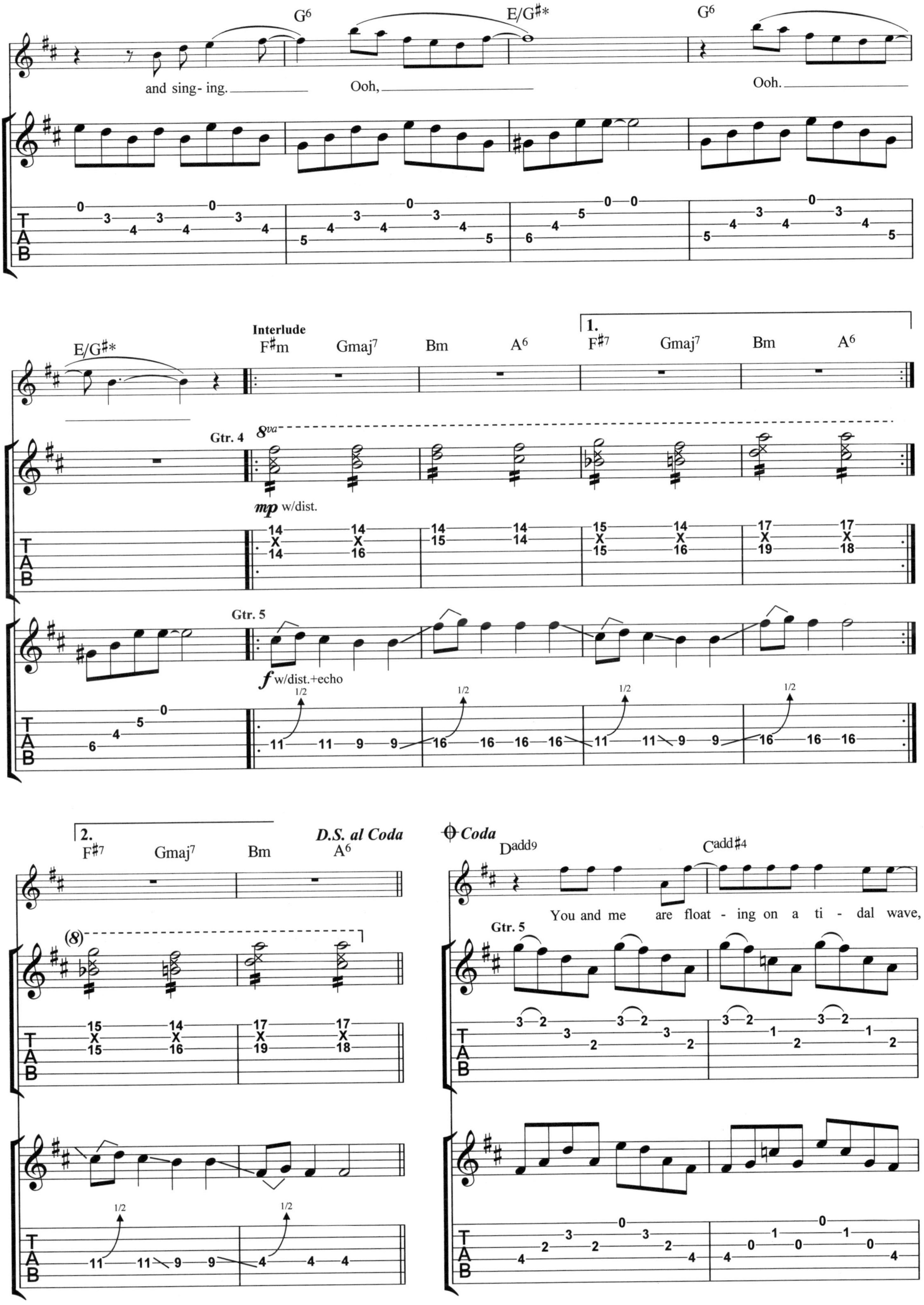
G6
E/G♯*
and sing- ing.
Ooh,
Ooh.
Interlude
F♯m
Gmaj7
Bm
A6
1.
F♯7
Gmaj7
Bm
A6
Gtr. 4
8va
mp w/dist.
Gtr. 5
f w/dist.+echo
1/2
2.
F♯7
Gmaj7
Bm
D.S. al Coda
A6
(8)
Coda
Dadd9
Cadd♯4
You and me are float- ing on a ti - dal wave,
Gtr. 5

E7
Dadd9
Cadd♯4
to-geth-er. You and me are drift - ing in-to out - er space,
E7
G6
E/G♯*
and sing-ing. Ooh,
Gtr. 6 dbls w/dist.

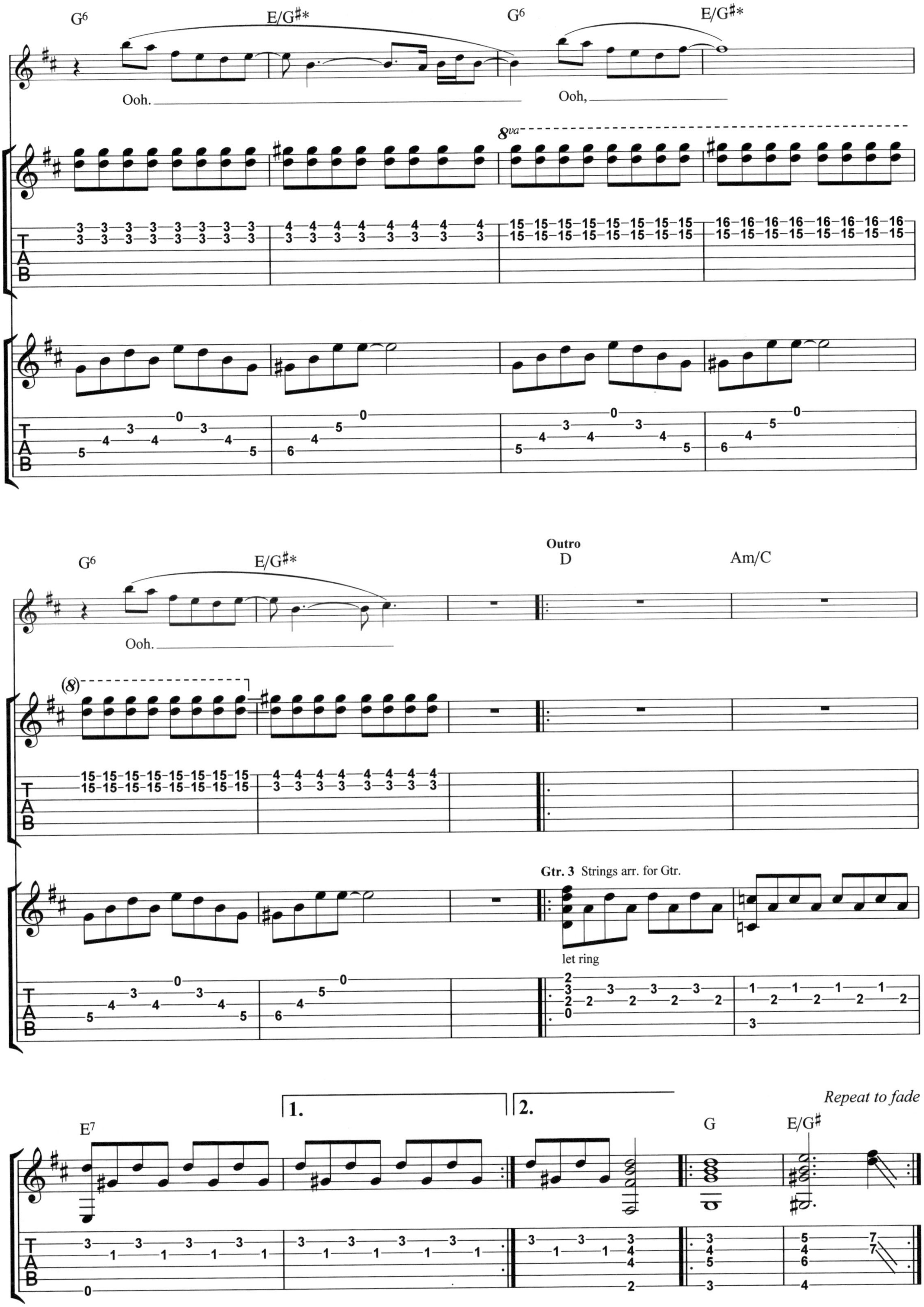
G6
E/G♯*
Ooh.
Ooh,
8va
(8)
Outro
D
Am/C
Gtr. 3 Strings arr. for Gtr.
let ring
E7
1.
2.
G
E/G♯
Repeat to fade
T
A
B

SPEED OF SOUND

Words & Music by Guy Berryman, Jon Buckland, Will Champion & Chris Martin

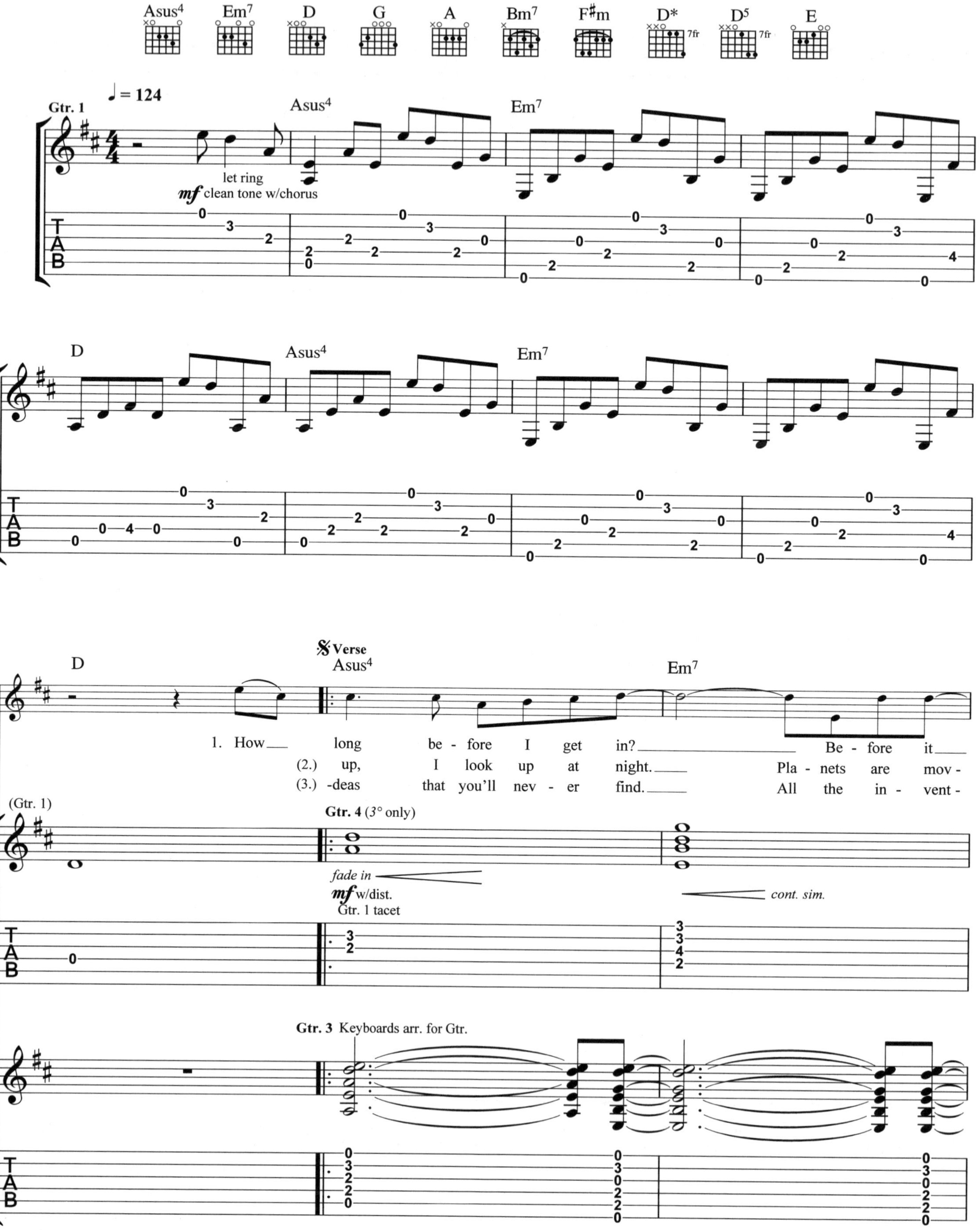

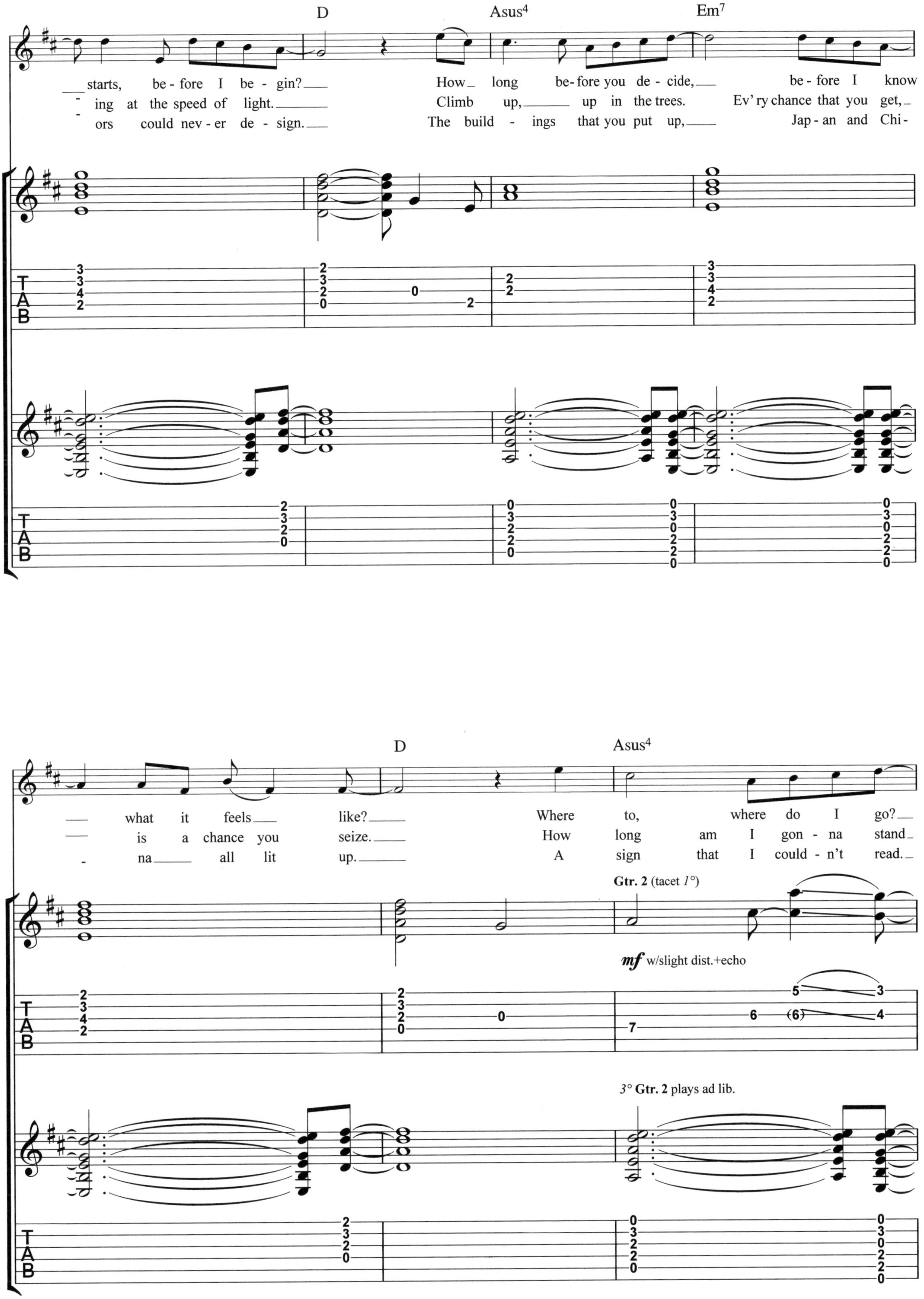
D
Asus4
Em7
starts, before I begin?
How long before you decide, before I know
ing at the speed of light.
Climb up, up in the trees. Ev'ry chance that you get,
ors could never design.
The buildings that you put up, Japan and Chi-
D
Asus4
what it feels like?
Where to, where do I go?
is a chance you seize.
How long am I gonna stand
na all lit up.
A sign that I couldn't read.
Gtr. 2 (tacet 1°)
mf w/slight dist.+echo
3° Gtr. 2 plays ad lib.

Em7
D
If you nev - er try then you'll nev - er know. How
with my head stuck un - der sand? I'll
Or a light that I could - n't see. Some
Asus4
Em7
D
long do I have to climb, up on the side of this moun-tain of mine?
start be - fore I can stop, be - fore I see things the right way up.
things you have to be - lieve, oth - ers are puz - zles, puz - zl - ing me.
Interlude
Gtr. 1
1.
Asus4
Em7
D
let ring
Gtr. 2 tacet

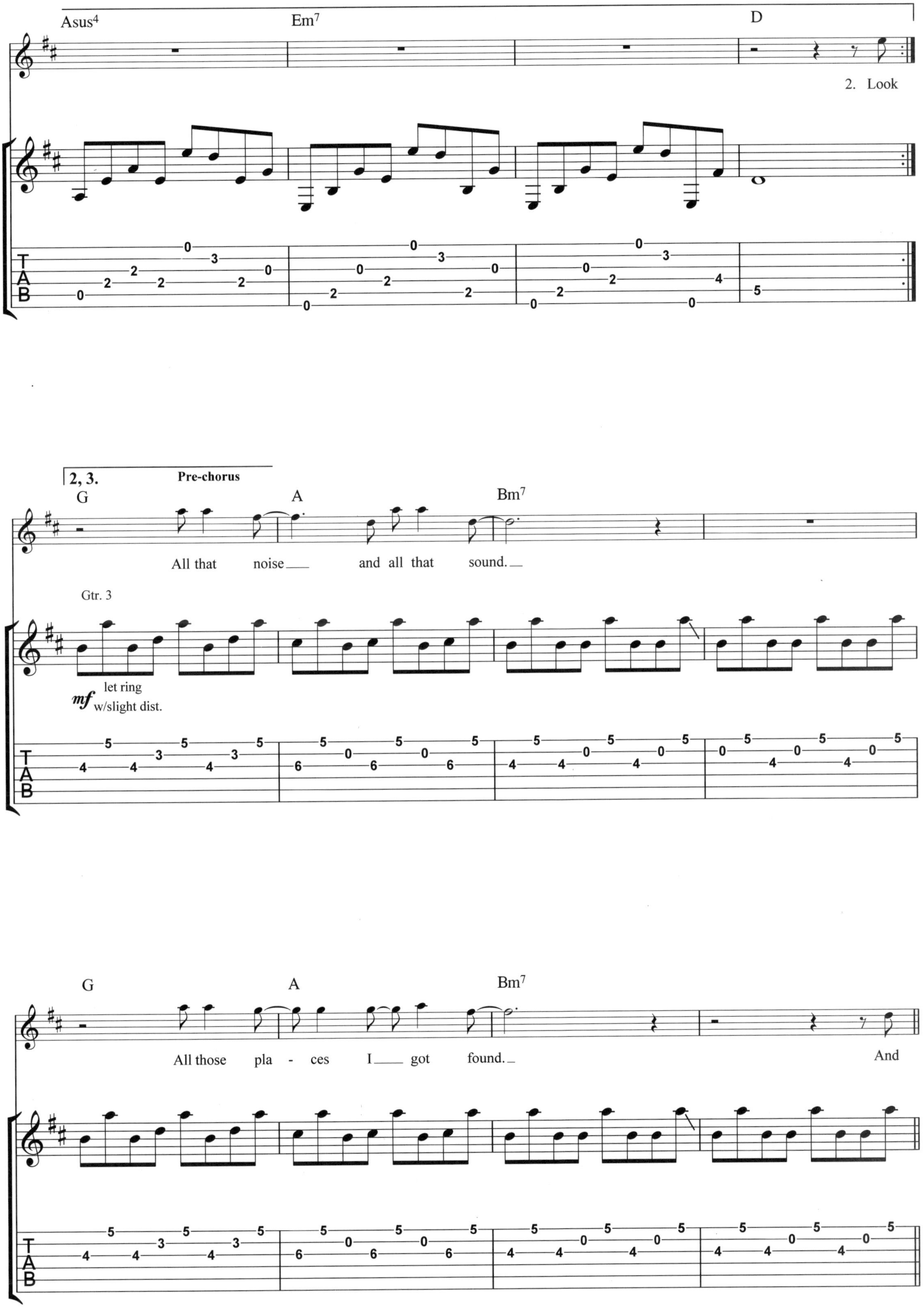
Asus4
Em7
D
2. Look
2, 3.
Pre-chorus
G
A
Bm7
All that noise and all that sound.
Gtr. 3
mf
let ring
w/slight dist.
G
A
Bm7
All those pla - ces I got found.
And
T
A
B

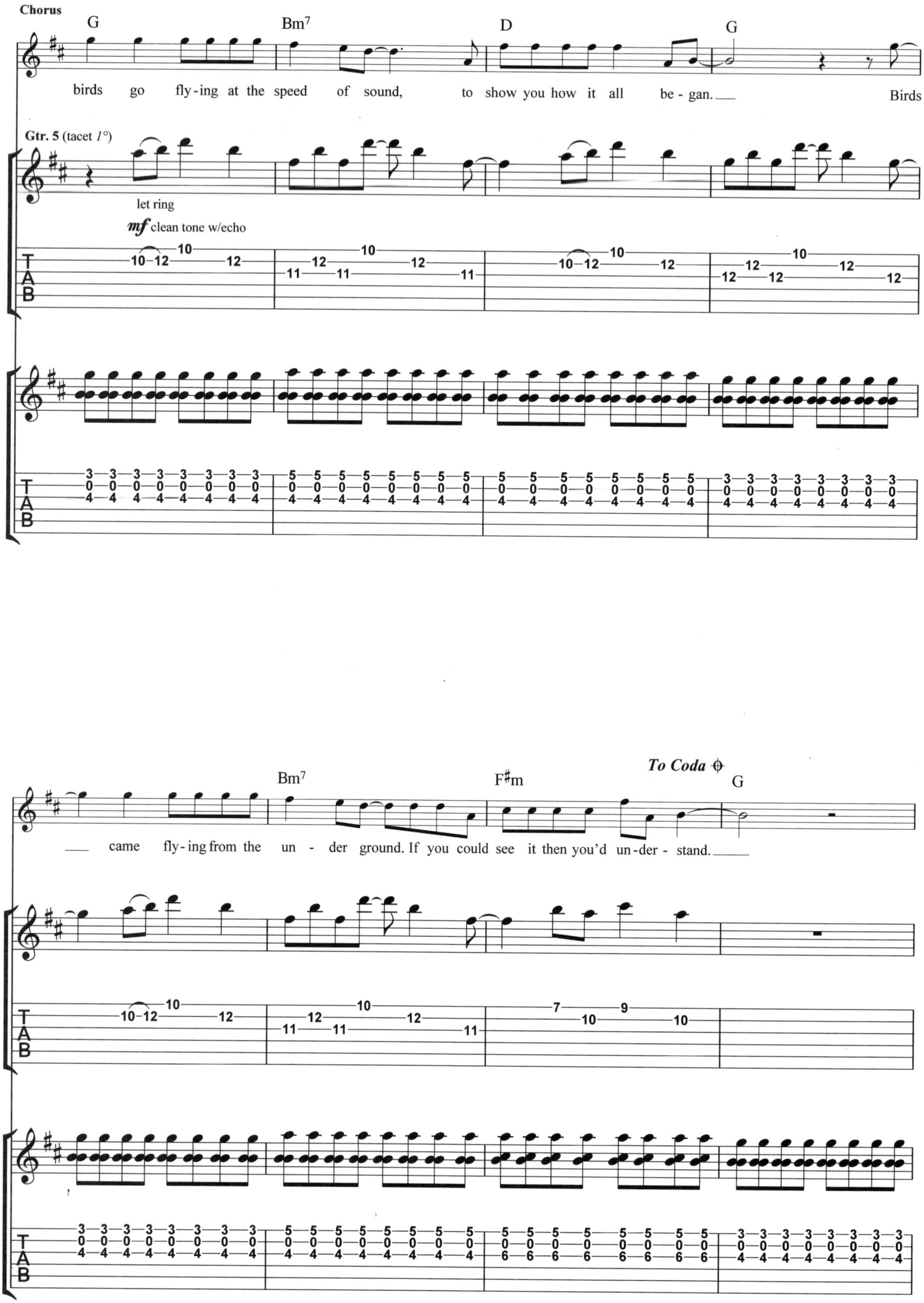
Chorus
G
Bm7
D
G
birds go fly-ing at the speed of sound, to show you how it all be-gan. Birds
Gtr. 5 (tacet 1°)
let ring
mf clean tone w/echo
To Coda
Bm7
F#m
G
came fly-ing from the un-der ground. If you could see it then you'd un-der-stand.

Interlude
Asus4
Em7
Gtr. 1
let ring
Gtr. 3 tacet
D
Asus4
Em7
D.S. al Coda
D
3. I -
Coda
G
F#m
G
Ah, when you see it then you'll un-der-stand.

Interlude
D*
Gtr. 4
fade in
cont. sim.
Gtrs. 3+5 tacet
Pre-chorus
D5
G
A
Bm7
All those signs, I knew what they meant. Some things you
Gtr. 3
let ring
Gtr. 4 tacet
E
can't in-vent. Some get made and some get sent, Ooh.

Chorus
E
G
Bm7
D
And birds go fly-ing at the speed of sound, to show you how it all be - gan.
Gtr. 5
TAB
G
Bm7
F♯m
Birds came fly-ing from the un - der - ground. If you could see it then you'd un - der - stand.

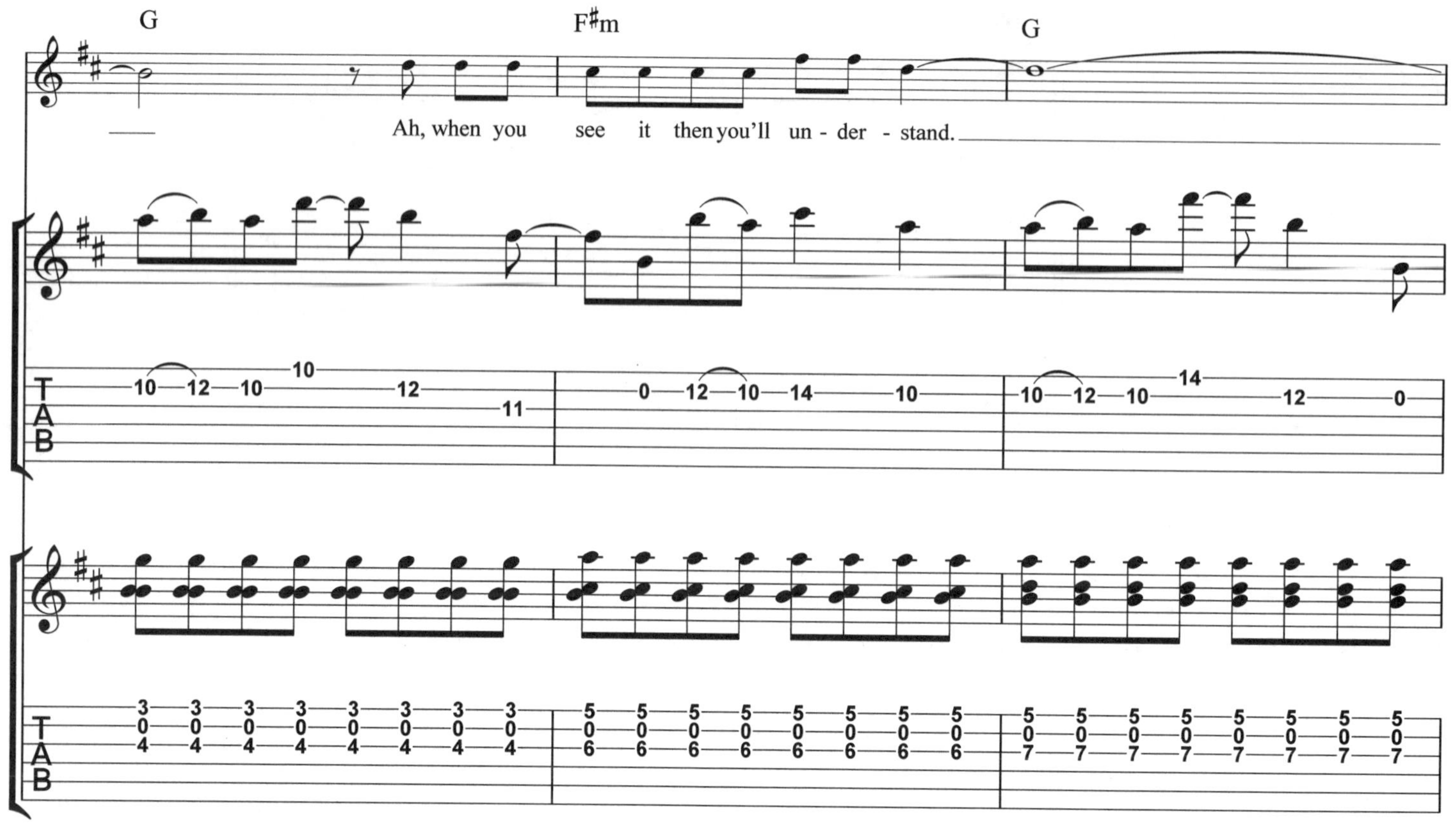
G
F♯m
G
Ah, when you see it then you'll un - der - stand.

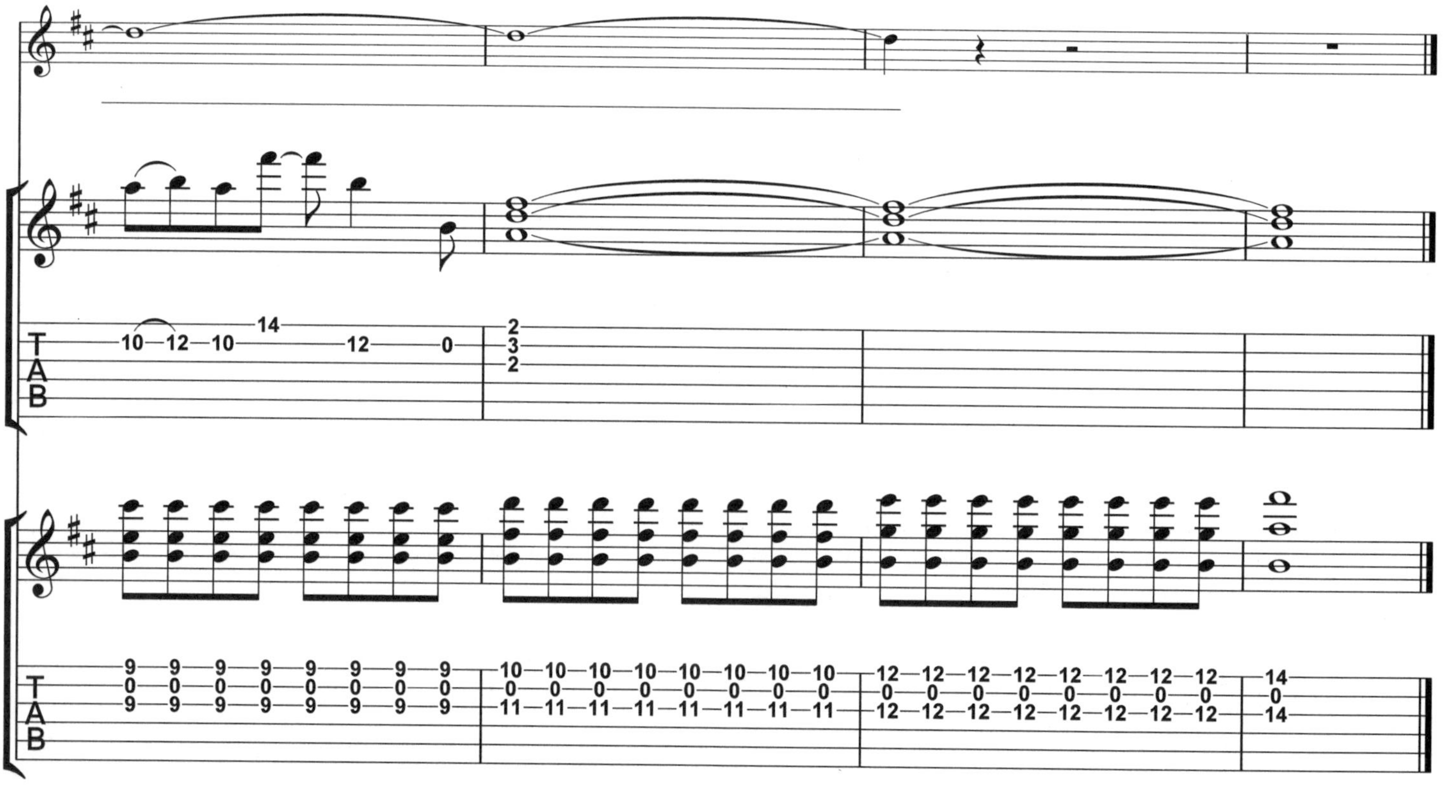

A MESSAGE

Words & Music by Guy Berryman, Jon Buckland, Will Champion & Chris Martin

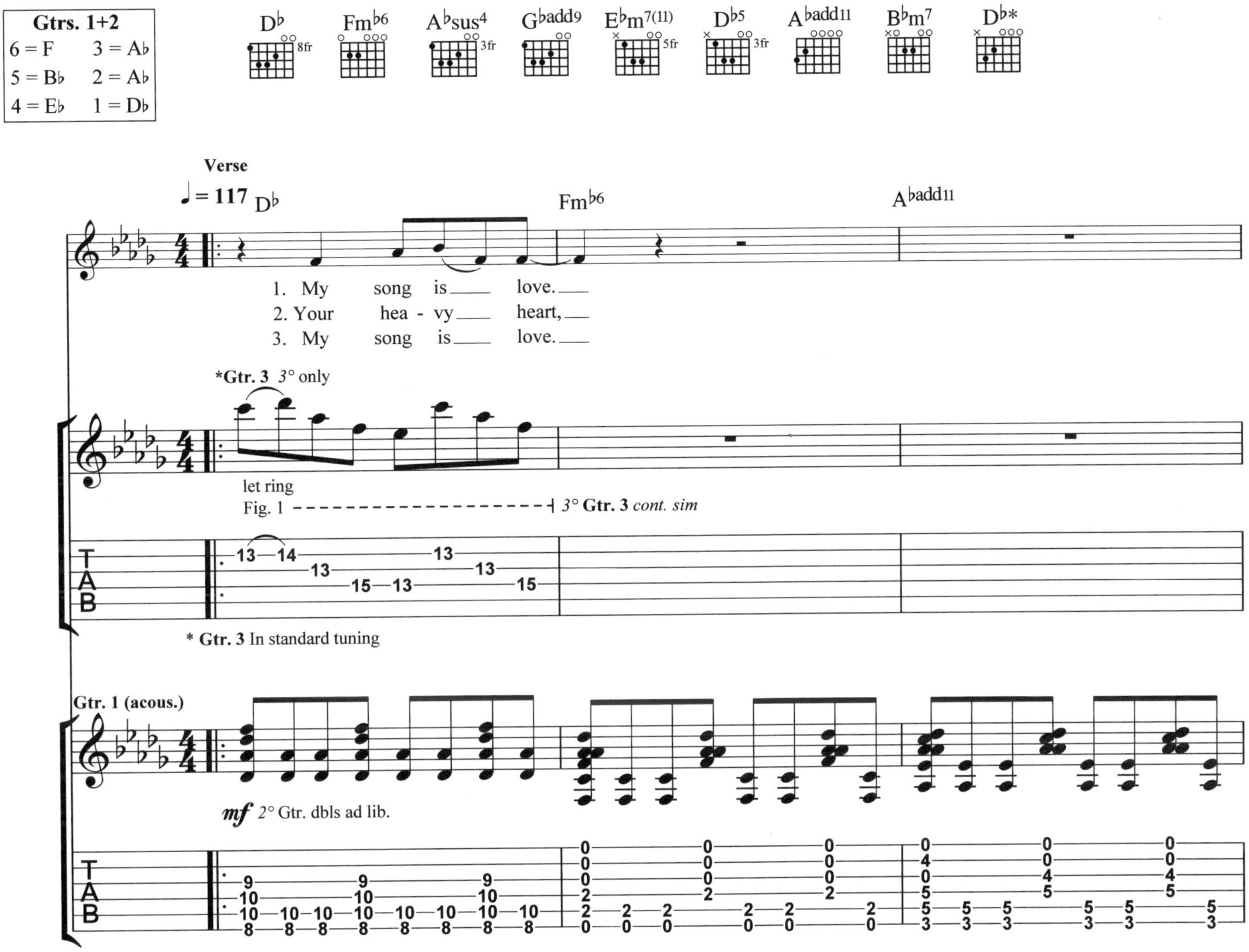

D♭
Fm♭6
A♭add11
And it goes up.
And it's so hard to see clear-ly.
And I'm on fire for you. clear-ly.
2° + 3°
1° only
Pre-chorus
G♭add9
Fm♭6
A♭add11
1, 3. You don't have to be a - lone.
2. You don't have to be on your own.
1.
2. 3.
G♭add9
Fm♭6
You don't have to be on your own.

Chorus
A♭add11
E♭m7(11)
And I'm not
go - ing to take it back.
D♭5
A♭add11
E♭m7(11)
And I'm not go - ing to say I don't mean that.
D♭5
A♭add11
E♭m7(11)
You're the tar - get that I'm aim -

D♭5
A♭add11
G♭add9
- - ing at.
And I'll get that mes -
And I'm no - - - thing on
Fm♭6
A♭add11
1.
- sage home.
my own.
Gtr. 3 (elec.)
mf w/slight dist. +echo
2.
A♭add11
G♭add9
Fm♭6
Got to get that mes - sage home.

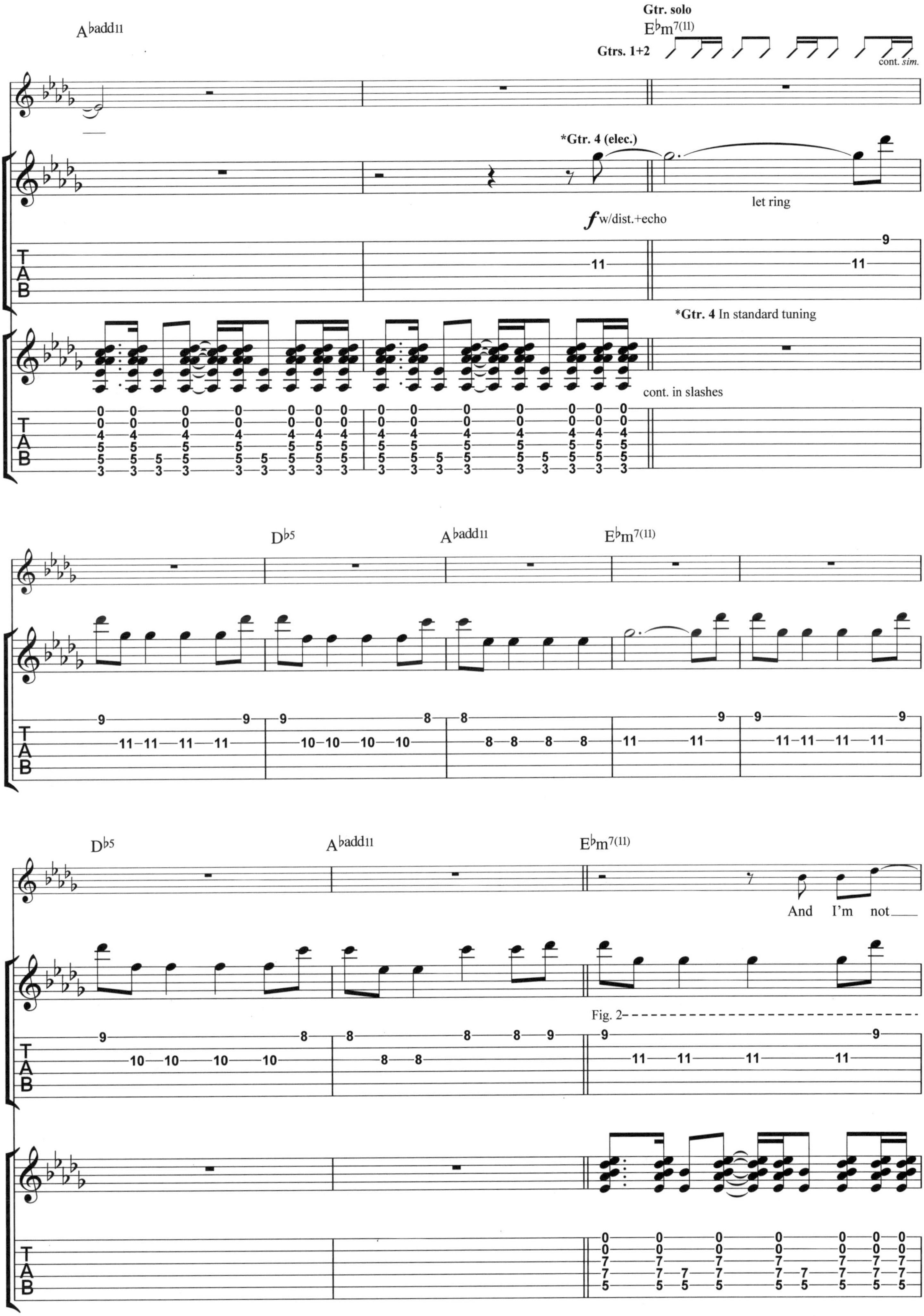
Gtr. solo
A♭add11
E♭m7(11)
Gtrs. 1+2
cont. sim.
*Gtr. 4 (elec.)
let ring
f w/dist.+echo
*Gtr. 4 In standard tuning
cont. in slashes
D♭5
A♭add11
E♭m7(11)
And I'm not
Fig. 2

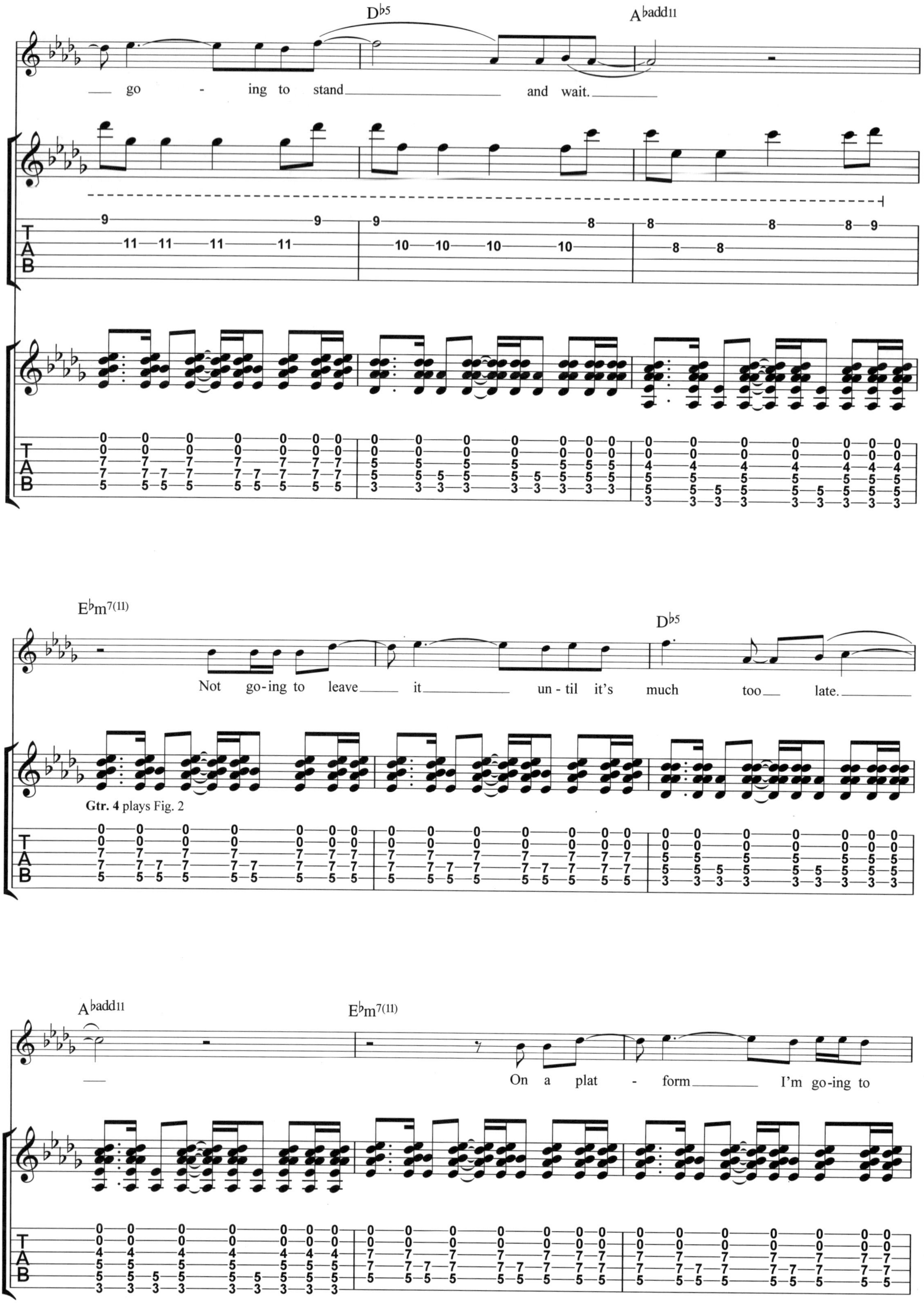
D♭5
A♭add11
go - ing to stand and wait.
E♭m7(11)
D♭5
Not go-ing to leave it un-til it's much too late.
Gtr. 4 plays Fig. 2
A♭add11
E♭m7(11)
On a plat - form I'm go-ing to

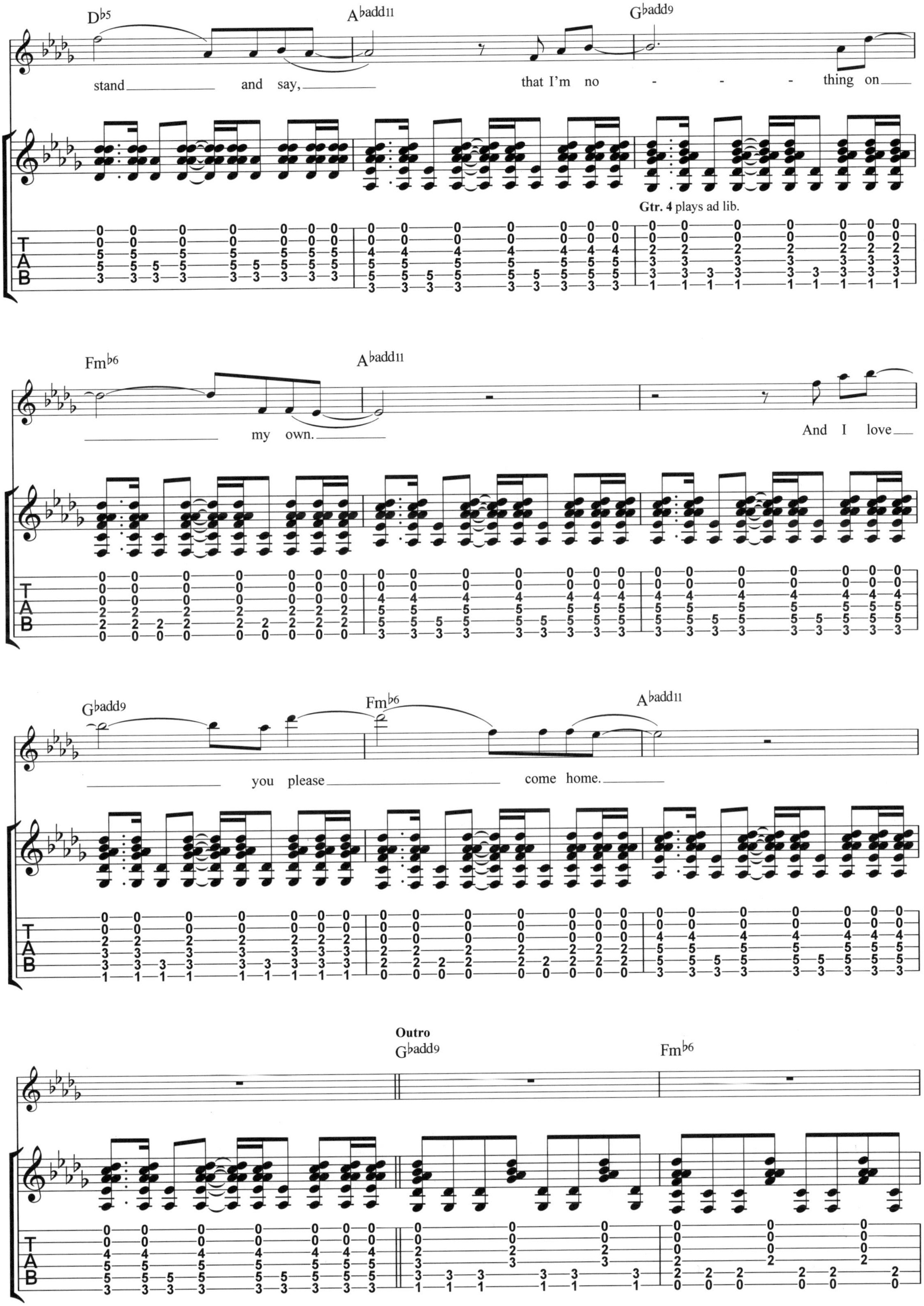
D♭5
A♭add11
G♭add9
stand and say, that I'm no - - - thing on
Gtr. 4 plays ad lib.
Fm♭6
A♭add11
my own. And I love
G♭add9
Fm♭6
A♭add11
you please come home.
Outro
G♭add9
Fm♭6

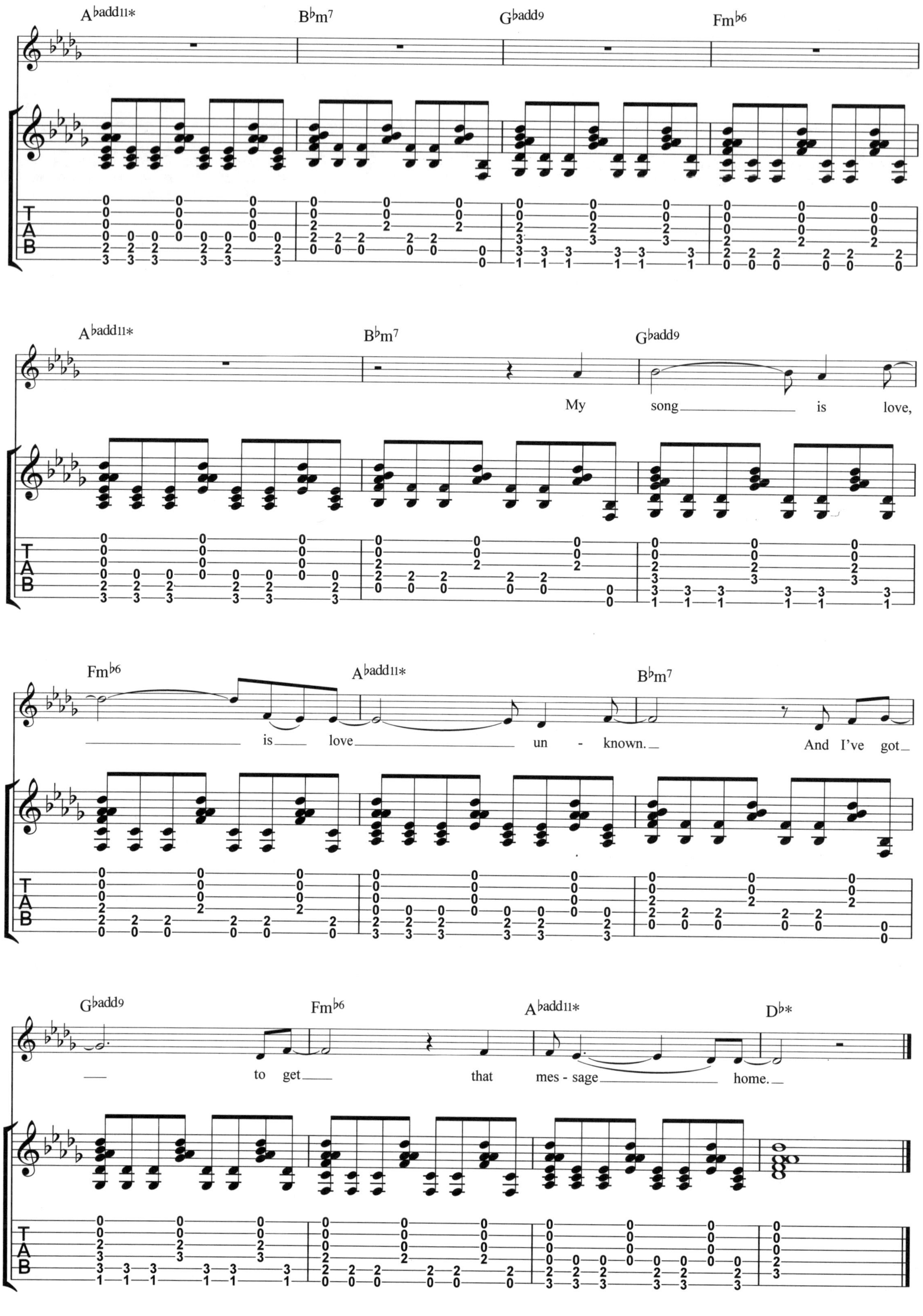
A♭add11*
B♭m7
G♭add9
Fm♭6
A♭add11*
B♭m7
G♭add9
My song is love,
Fm♭6
A♭add11*
B♭m7
is love un - known.
And I've got
G♭add9
Fm♭6
A♭add11*
D♭*
to get that mes - sage home.

LOW

Words & Music by Guy Berryman, Jon Buckland, Will Champion & Chris Martin

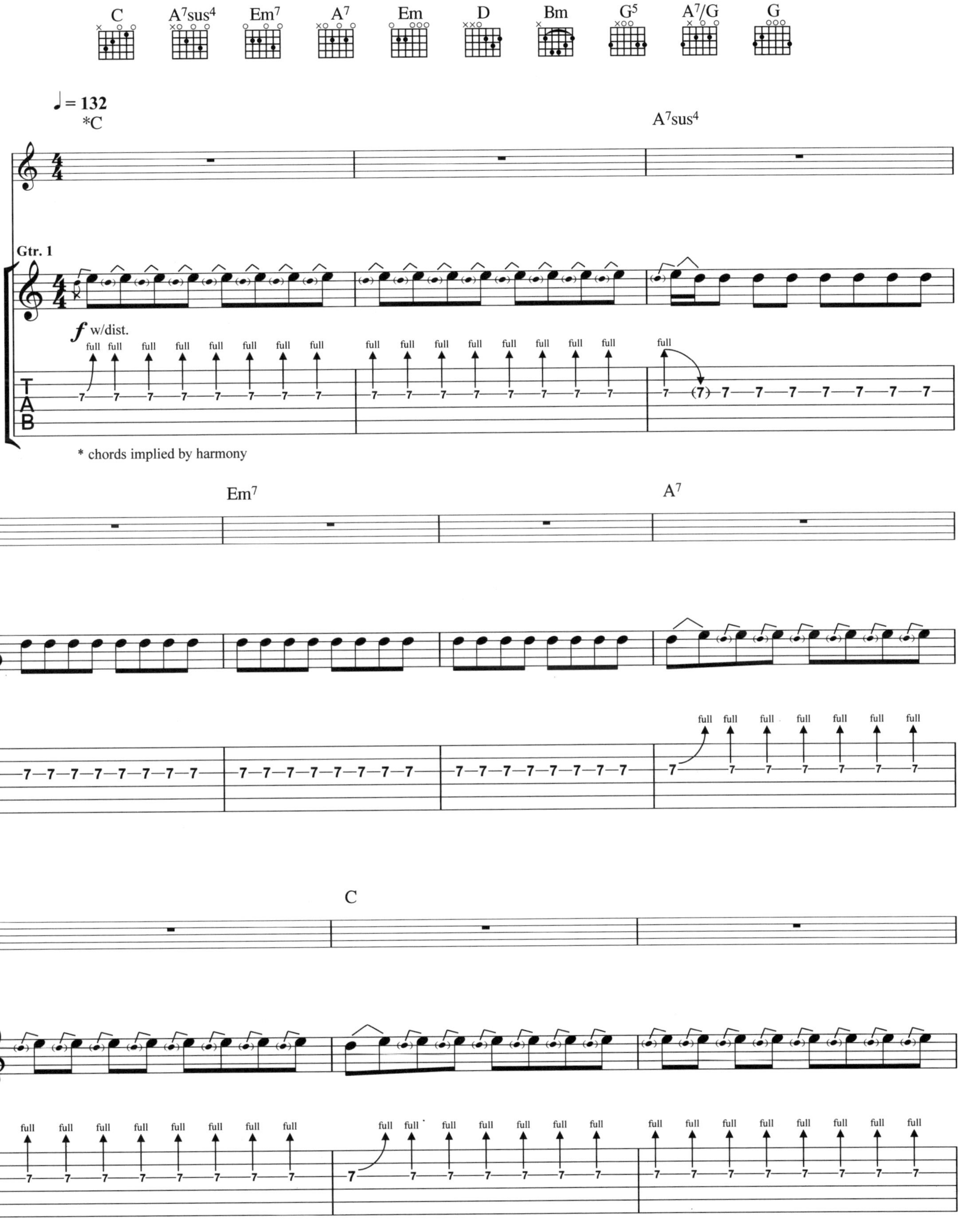

Verse
Em
D
1. You see the world in black and white.
2. The sky could fall, could fall on me.
Gtr. 2
full
mf clean tone
Bm
C
A7sus4
No co - lour, or light.
The part - - ing of the sea.
Em
D
You think you'll nev - er get it right.
But you mean more, mean more to me,
Bm
C
A7sus4
But you're wrong, you might.
than a - ny co - lour I can see.

Em
1.
2.
let ring
𝄋 Chorus
C
All you ever want - ed was love,
Gtr. 1
full
A7sus4
but you never looked hard e - nough.
Em7
It's never gonna give it - self up.
A7
C
All you ev - er

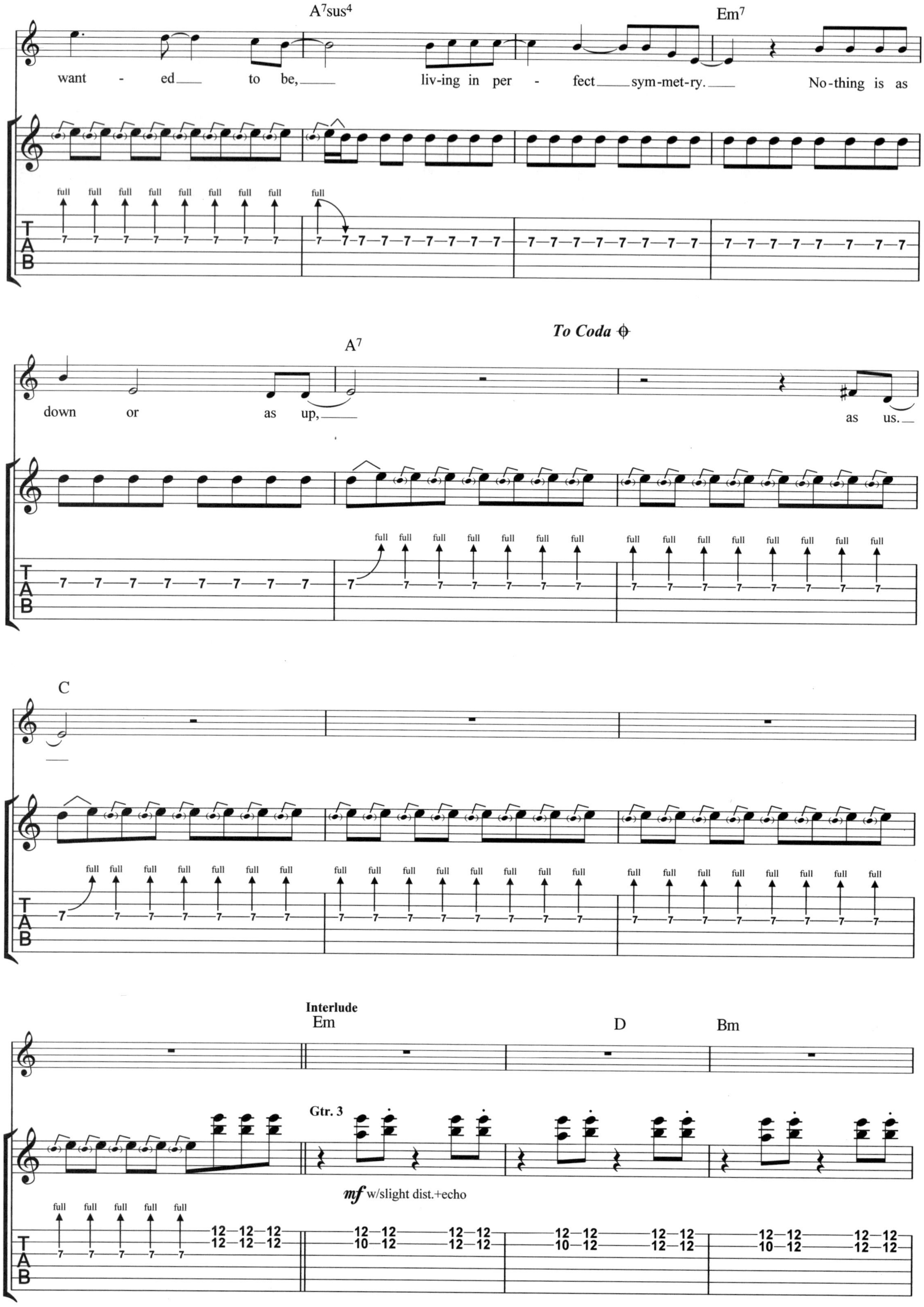
A7sus4
Em7
want - ed to be, liv-ing in per - fect sym-met-ry. No-thing is as
To Coda
A7
down or as up, as us.
C
Interlude
Em
D
Bm
Gtr. 3
mf w/slight dist.+echo

C
A7sus4
Em
Verse
Em
D
Bm
(3.) You see the world in black and white,
Gtr. 2
C
A7sus4
Em
not paint - - ed right.
Em
D
You see no mean - ing to your life.

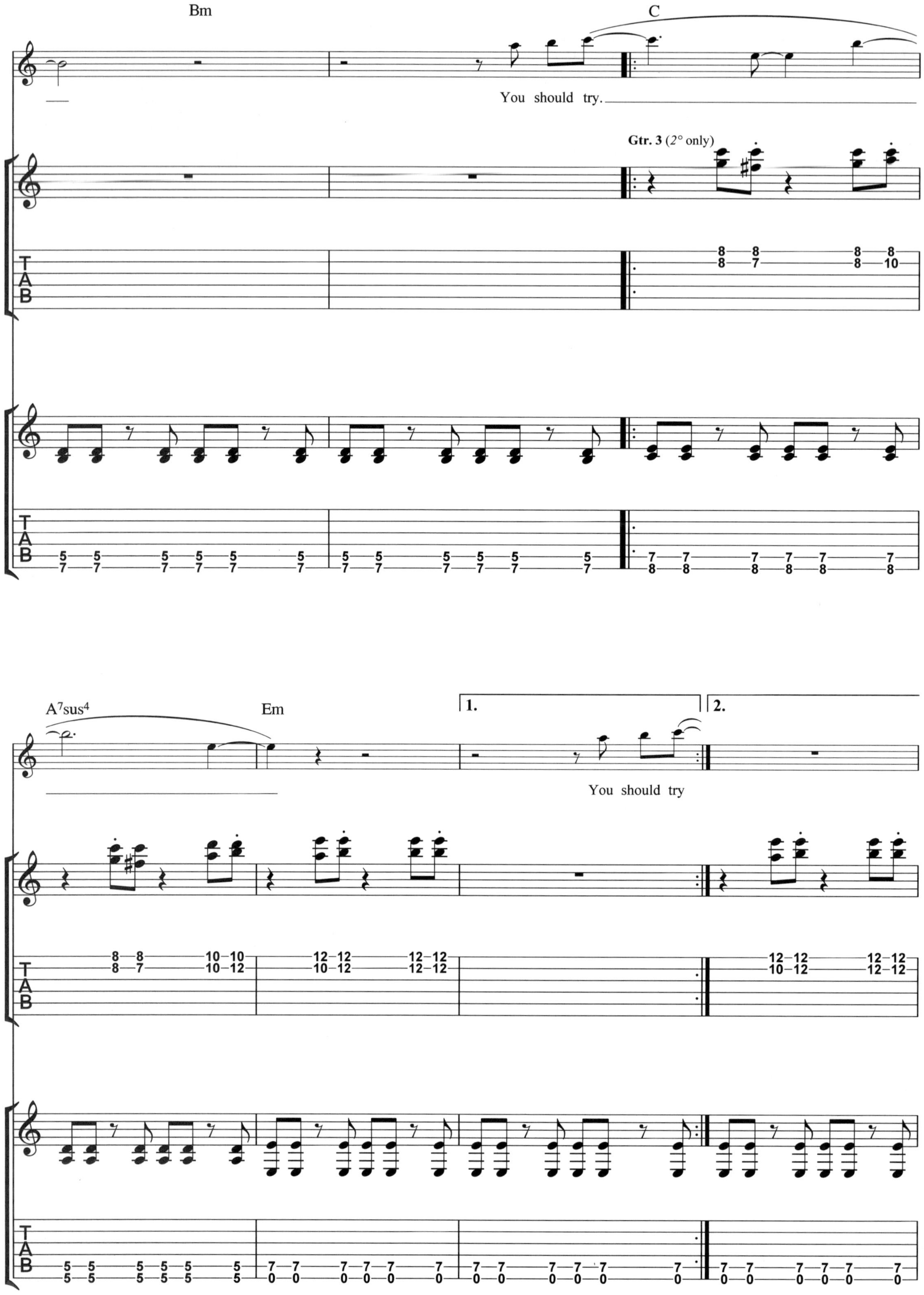
Bm
C
You should try.
Gtr. 3 (2° only)
A7sus4
Em
1.
2.
You should try

D.S. al Coda
Coda
C
A7sus4
Don't you want to see it come soon, float - ing in a
Don't you want to see it come down. There for throw-ing
Em7
big white bal - loon. Fly - ing in your own sil - ver spoon.
your arms a - round. Say - ing "you're not a mo - ment too soon".

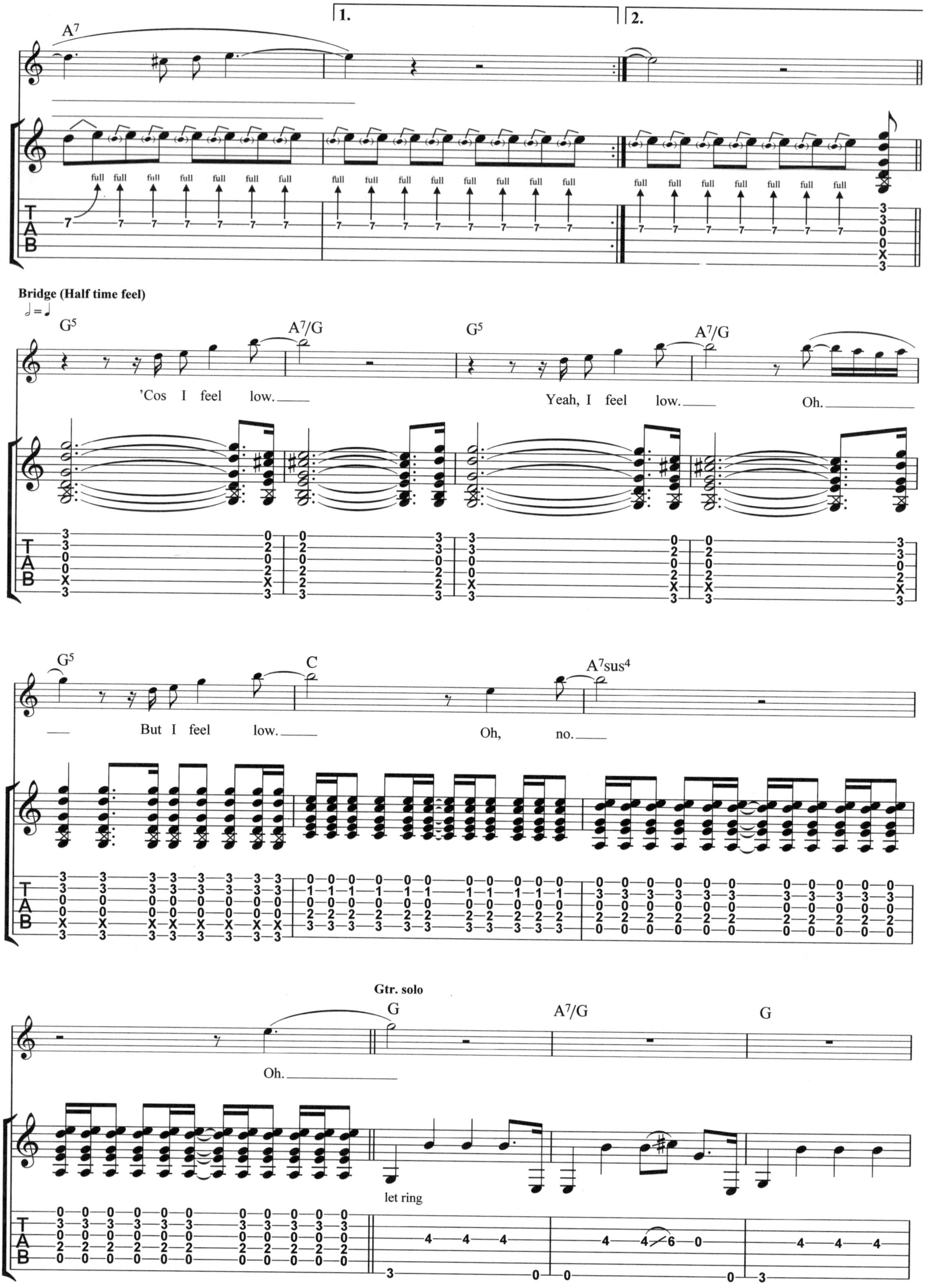
1.
2.
A7
full
Bridge (Half time feel)
G5
A7/G
'Cos I feel low.
Yeah, I feel low.
Oh.
But I feel low.
C
A7sus4
Oh, no.
Oh.
Gtr. solo
G
let ring
T
A
B

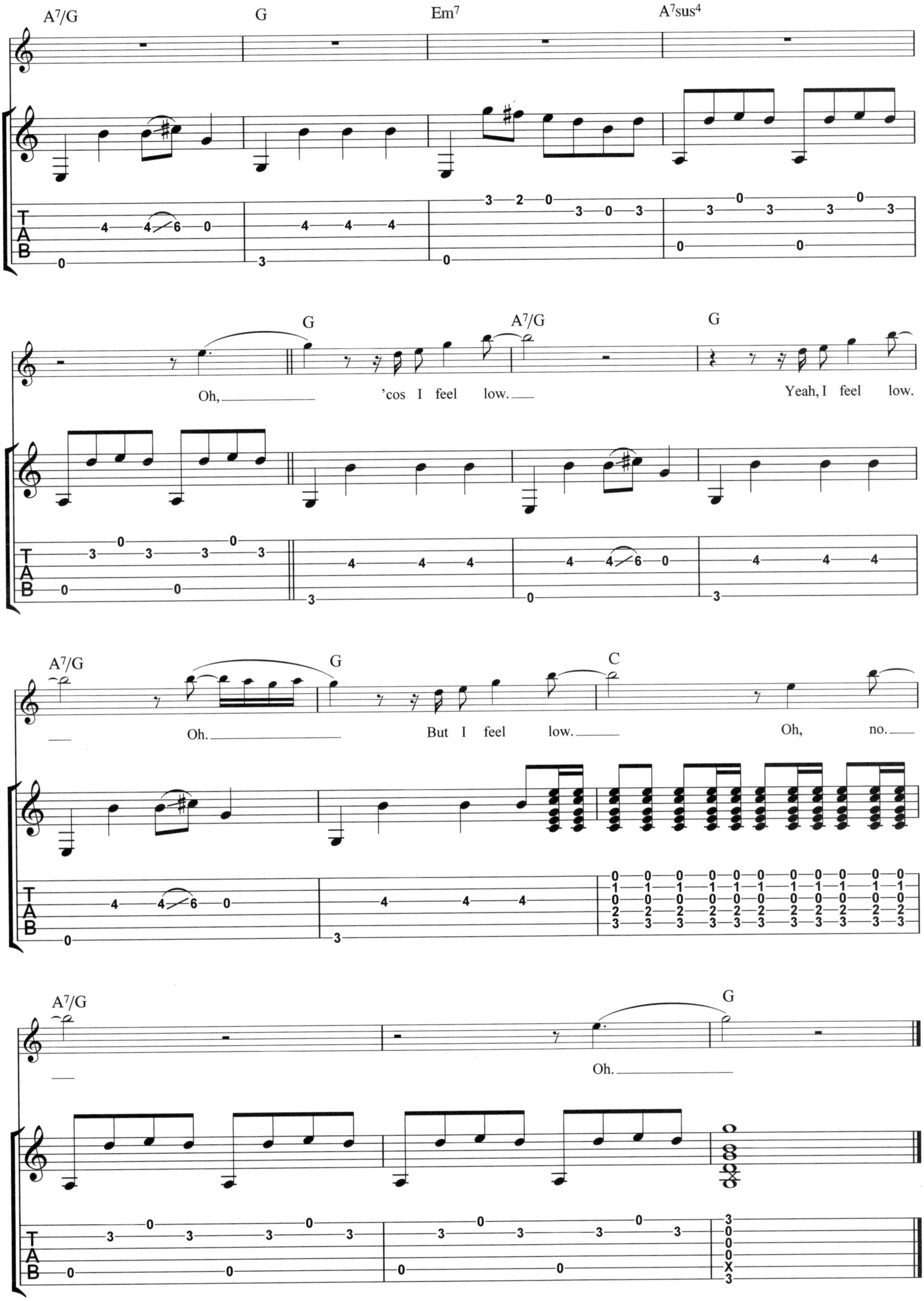
A7/G
G
Em7
A7sus4
G
A7/G
G
Oh, 'cos I feel low.
Yeah, I feel low.
A7/G
G
C
Oh. But I feel low. Oh, no.
A7/G
G
Oh.

THE HARDEST PART

Words & Music by Guy Berryman, Jon Buckland, Will Champion & Chris Martin

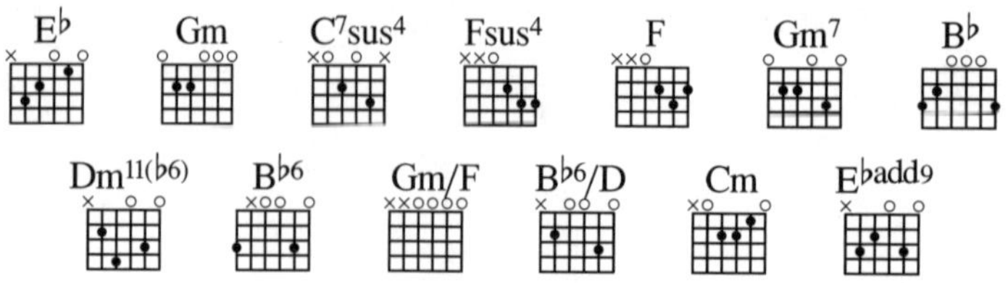

Capo 3rd Fret

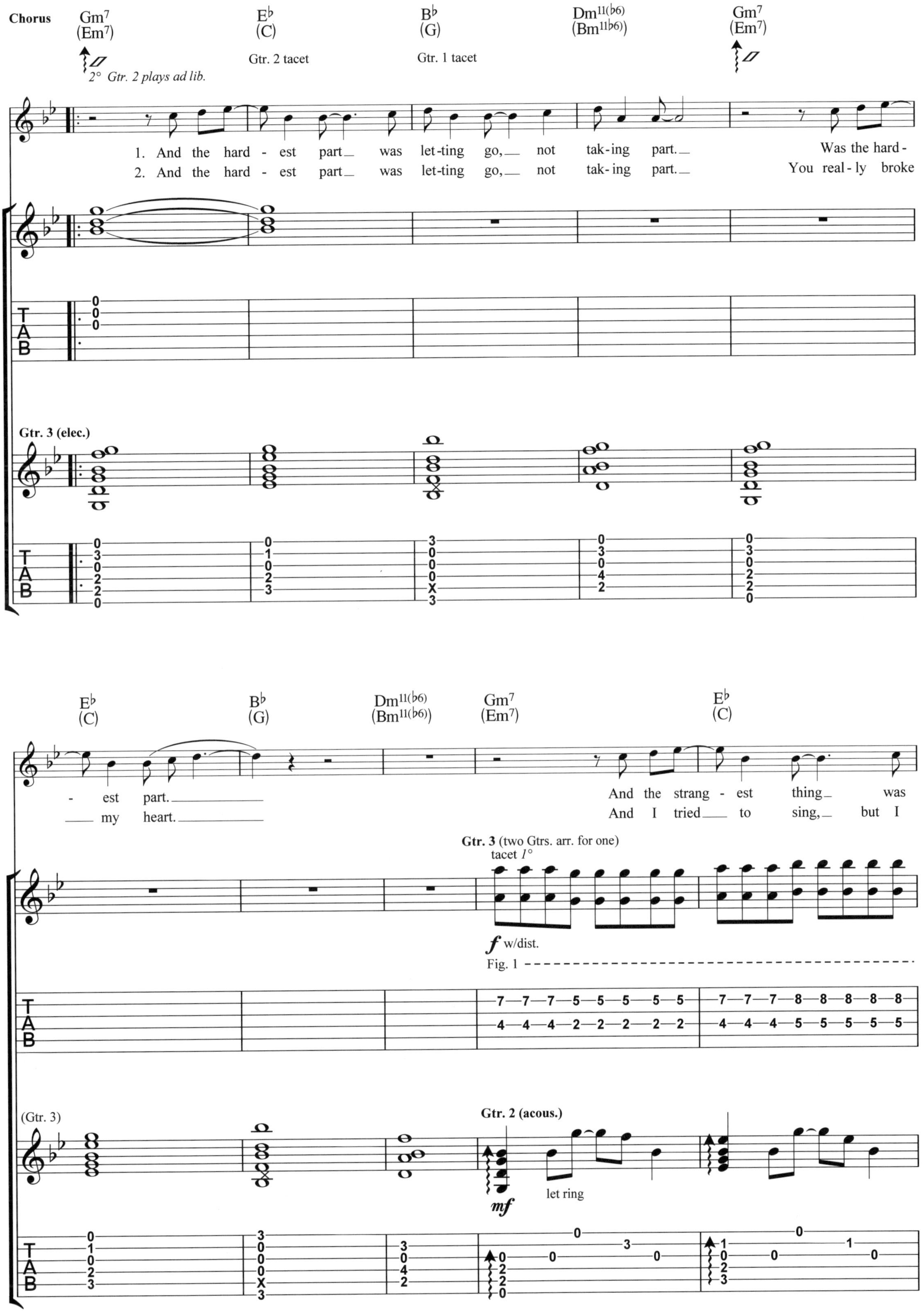
Chorus
Gm7 (Em7)
Eb (C)
Bb (G)
Dm11(b6) (Bm11(b6))
Gm7 (Em7)
2° Gtr. 2 plays ad lib.
Gtr. 2 tacet
Gtr. 1 tacet
1. And the hard - est part was let-ting go, not tak-ing part. Was the hard -
2. And the hard - est part was let-ting go, not tak-ing part. You real-ly broke
Gtr. 3 (elec.)
Eb (C)
Bb (G)
Dm11(b6) (Bm11(b6))
Gm7 (Em7)
Eb (C)
- est part.
my heart.
And the strang - est thing was
And I tried to sing, but I
Gtr. 3 (two Gtrs. arr. for one)
tacet 1°
f w/dist.
Fig. 1
(Gtr. 3)
Gtr. 2 (acous.)
mf
let ring

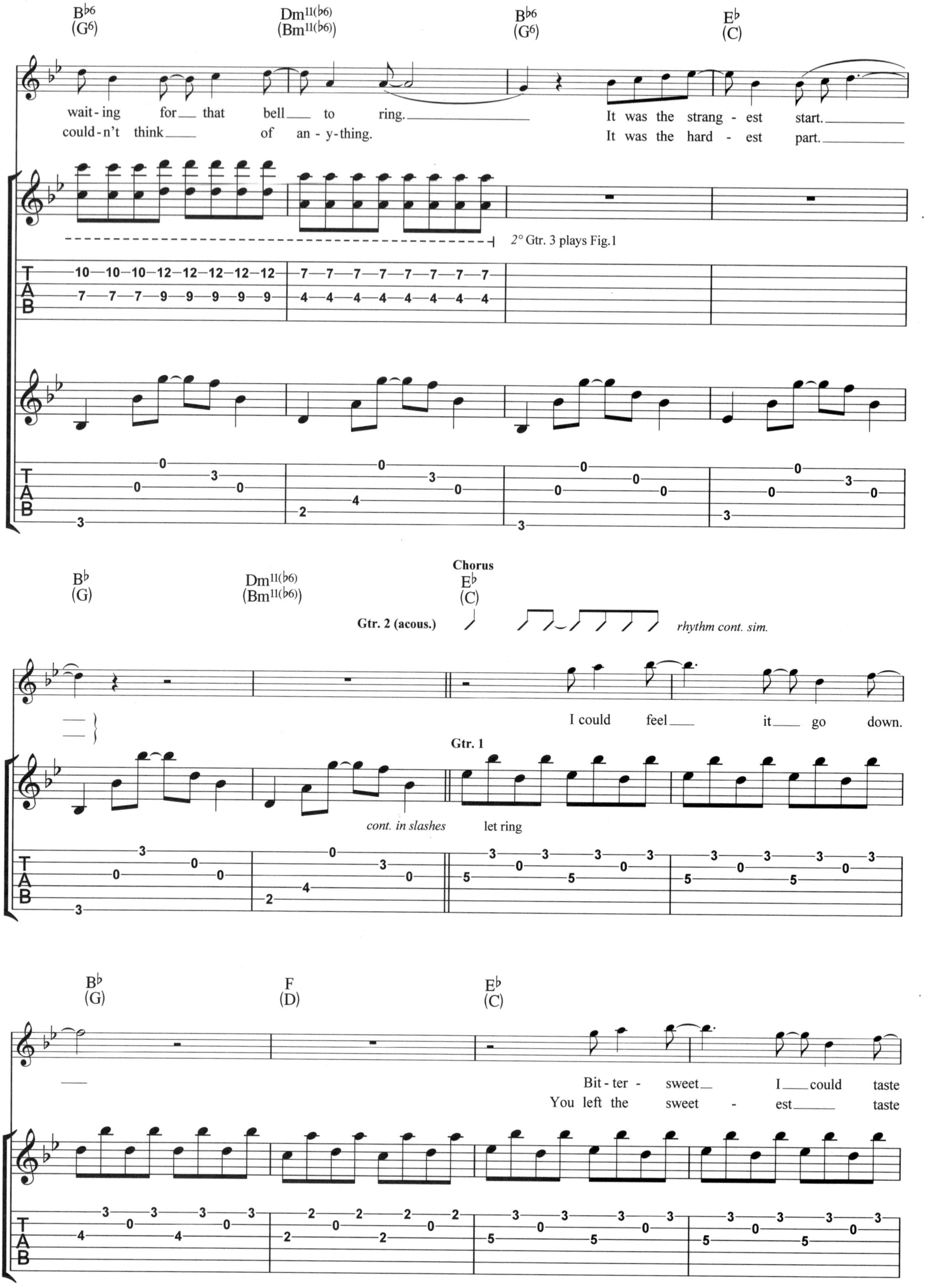
B♭6 (G6)
Dm11(♭6) (Bm11(♭6))
B♭6 (G6)
E♭ (C)
wait-ing for that bell to ring. It was the strang - est start.
could-n't think of an - y-thing. It was the hard - est part.
2° Gtr. 3 plays Fig.1
B♭ (G)
Dm11(♭6) (Bm11(♭6))
Chorus
E♭ (C)
Gtr. 2 (acous.)
rhythm cont. sim.
I could feel it go down.
Gtr. 1
cont. in slashes
let ring
B♭ (G)
F (D)
E♭ (C)
Bit-ter - sweet I could taste
You left the sweet - est taste

B♭ (G)
F (D)
E♭ (C)
in my mouth.
in my mouth.
Sil-ver lin - ing, the clouds.
Gm (Em)
Gm/F (Em/D)
B♭6/D (G6/B)
1.
Cm (Am)
Oh, and I,
I
Interlude
Gm7 (Em7)
E♭add9 (Cadd9)
Dm11(♭6) (Bm11(♭6))
rhythm cont. sim.
wish that I could work it out.
Gtr. 4
mf w/slight dist.+echo
w/bar
TAB
-1/2

Gm7 (Em7)
E♭add9 (Cadd9)
B♭ (G)
Dm11(♭6) (Bm11(♭6))
2.
Cm (Am)
w/bar
-1/2
Gm (Em)
Gm/F (Em/D)
E♭ (C)
B♭6/D (G6/B)
F (D)
Oh, and I,
I won-der what it's all a-bout.
Interlude
E♭ (C)
Gm (Em)
C7sus4 (A7sus4)
E♭ (C)
let ring

Gm (Em)
C7sus4 (A7sus4)
E♭ (C)
I won-der what it's all a - bout.
Gtr. 4

Gm (Em)
C7sus4 (A7sus4)
E♭ (C)

Bridge
F
(D)
E♭
(C)
Ev-'ry-thing I know is_
Fig. 2
Gm
(Em)
C7sus4
(A7sus4)
E♭
(C)
wrong._
Ev-'ry-thing I do, it just comes
Fig. 2
Gtr. 4 plays Fig.2

Gm (Em)
C7sus4 (A7sus4)
E♭ (C)
Gm (Em)
un - done.
Ev-'ry-thing is torn a - - part.
C7sus4 (A7sus4)
E♭ (C)
Oh, and that's the hard - est part.
That's the
Gtr. 4

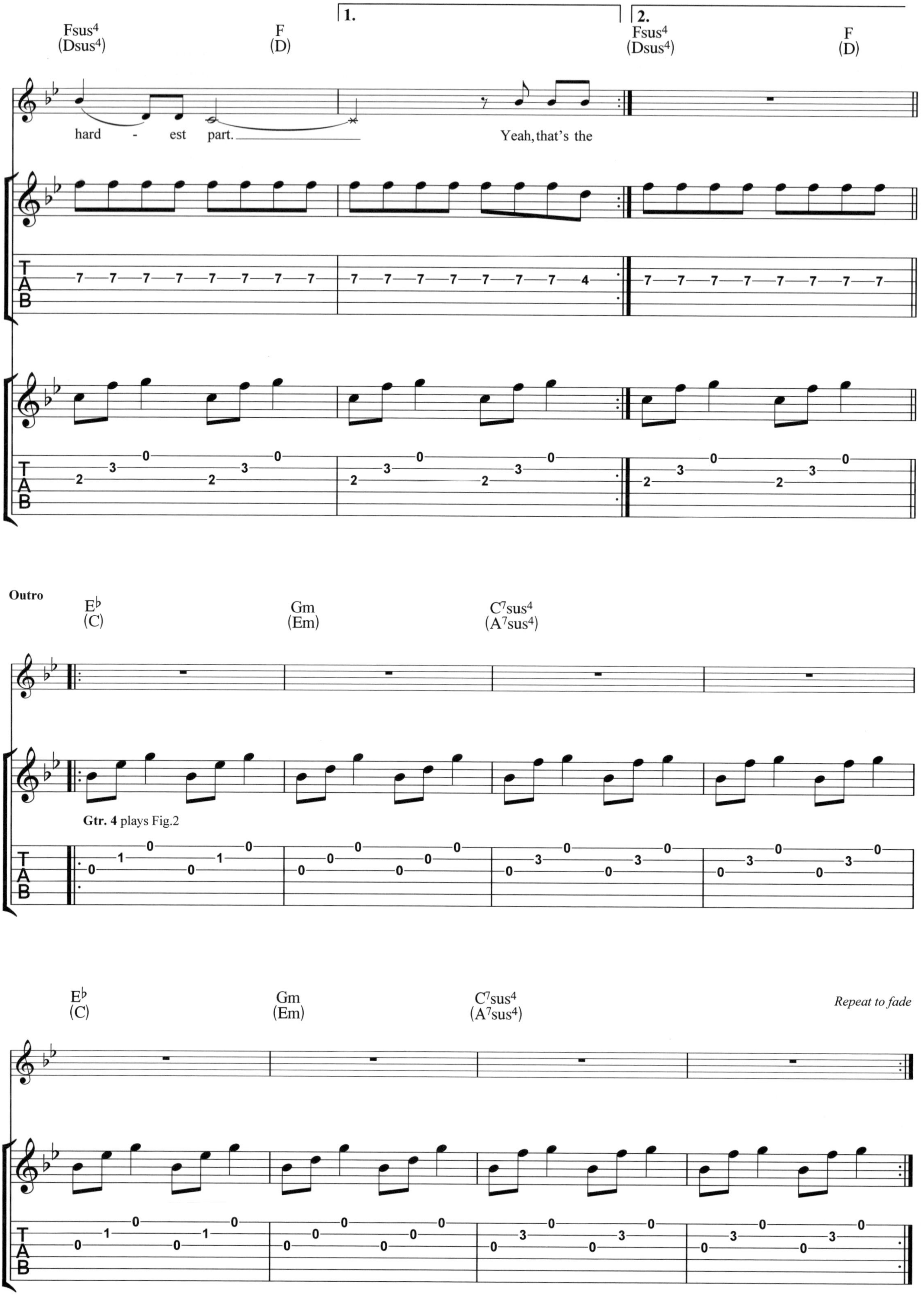

1.
2.
Fsus4 (Dsus4)
F (D)
hard - est part.
Yeah, that's the
Outro
E♭ (C)
Gm (Em)
C7sus4 (A7sus4)
Gtr. 4 plays Fig.2
Repeat to fade

SWALLOWED IN THE SEA

Words & Music by Guy Berryman, Jon Buckland, Will Champion & Chris Martin

Chorus
C F6 C Am G6
only blame me. And I could write a song, a hundred miles long. Well
Gtr. 2 plays ad lib.
Fmaj7 C G6
that's where I belong. And you belong with me. And
F6 C Am G6 Fmaj7 C
I could write it down or spread it all around. Get lost and then get found. Or
G6 C
swallowed in the sea.
2. You

Verse
Gtr. 2 tacet
C G6* F6 C
put me on a line and hung me out to dry. And
Gtr. 1 (acous.)
mf
G6* Fmaj7 C G6*
darl-ing that's when I de-cide to go see. You cut me down to size and op-
F C G6* Fmaj7
-ened up my eyes. Made me re-al-ize What I
C
could not see. And I
Chorus
F C
Gtr. 2 plays ad lib.
could write a book. The one
cont. in slashes

Am G6* Fmaj7 C
they'll say that shook the world and then it took,
G6* F C
took it back from me. And I could write it down, or
Am G6* Fmaj7 C
spread it all a - round. Get lost and then get found. And
G6* Fmaj7 C
you'll come back to me. Not swal - lowed in the sea.
cont. in slashes
TAB

Interlude
Dm Fmaj7 C G6*
Gtr. 2 tacet
Gtr. 3
rhythm cont. sim.
Tacet 1°
Ooh,
Gtr. 2
mf w/dist.
Dm Fmaj7
1. C G6*
2. C G6*
Ooh,
And I
Chorus
F C Am G6*
Gtr. 3 tacet
Gtr. 2 plays ad lib.
could write a song, a hun - dred miles long. Well
Gtr. 1 (acous.)
Fmaj7 C G6*
that's where I be - long. And you be - long with me. The streets

F C Am G6*
you're walk - ing on, a thou - sand hous - es long. Well
Fmaj7 C G6*
that's where I be - long, and you be - long with me. Ah, what good
F C Am G6*
is it to live, with no - thing left to give. For - get
Fmaj7 C G6*
but not for - give. Not lov - ing all you see. Ah, the streets

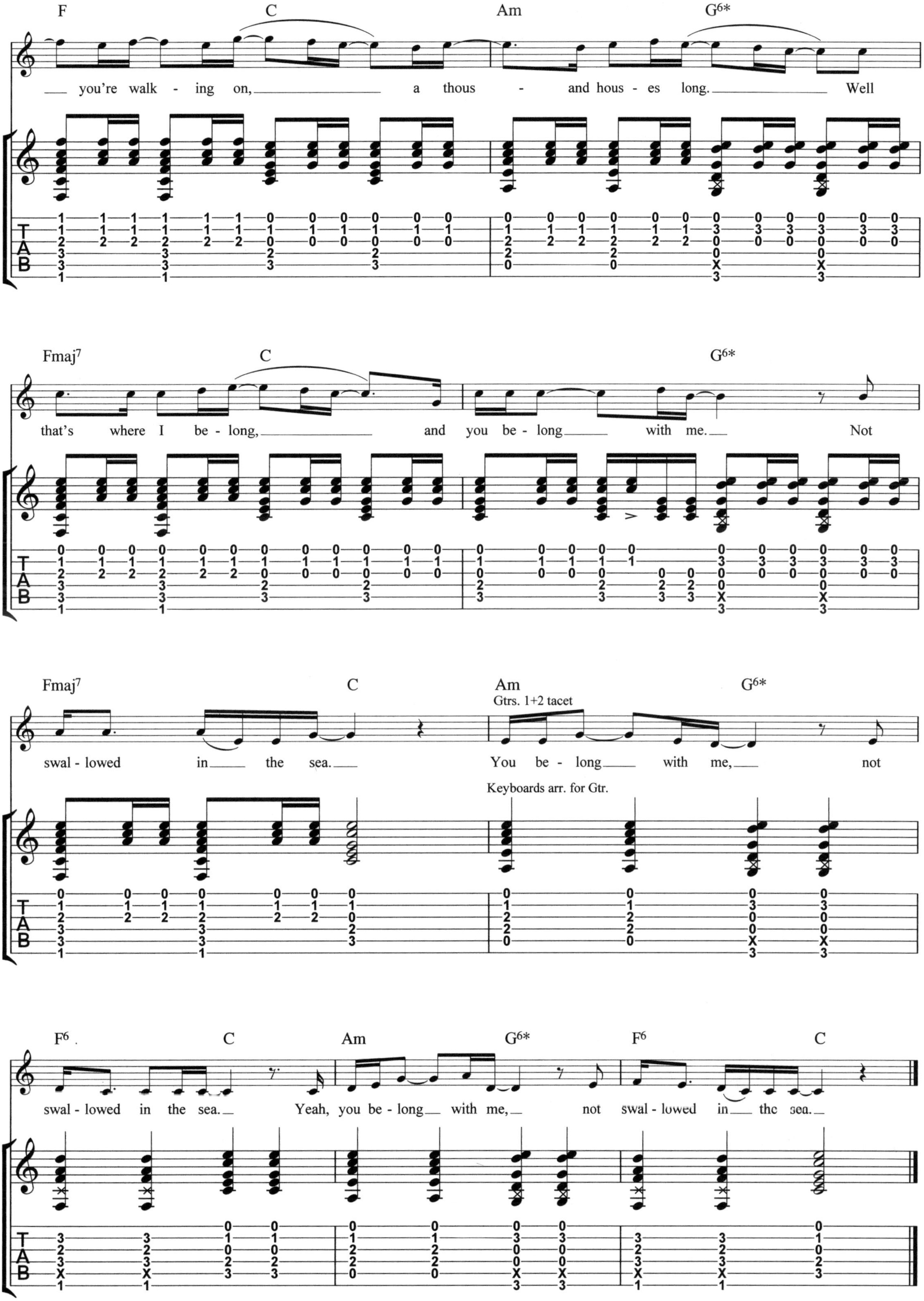
F C Am G6*
you're walk - ing on, a thous - and hous - es long. Well
Fmaj7 C G6*
that's where I be - long, and you be - long with me. Not
Fmaj7 C Am G6*
Gtrs. 1+2 tacet
swal - lowed in the sea. You be - long with me, not
Keyboards arr. for Gtr.
F6 C Am G6* F6 C
swal - lowed in the sea. Yeah, you be - long with me, not swal - lowed in the sea.

TWISTED LOGIC

Words & Music by Guy Berryman, Jon Buckland, Will Champion & Chris Martin

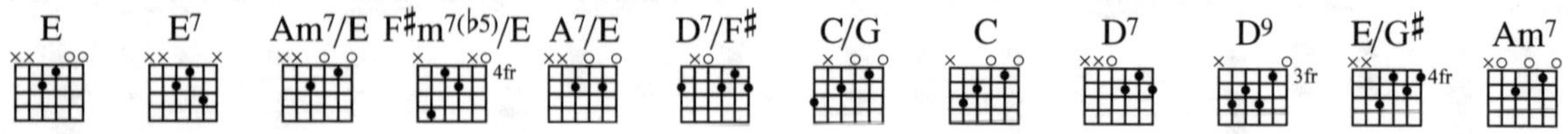

Gtrs. 1+2	
6 = E♭	3 = G♭
5 = A♭	2 = B♭
4 = D♭	1 = E♭

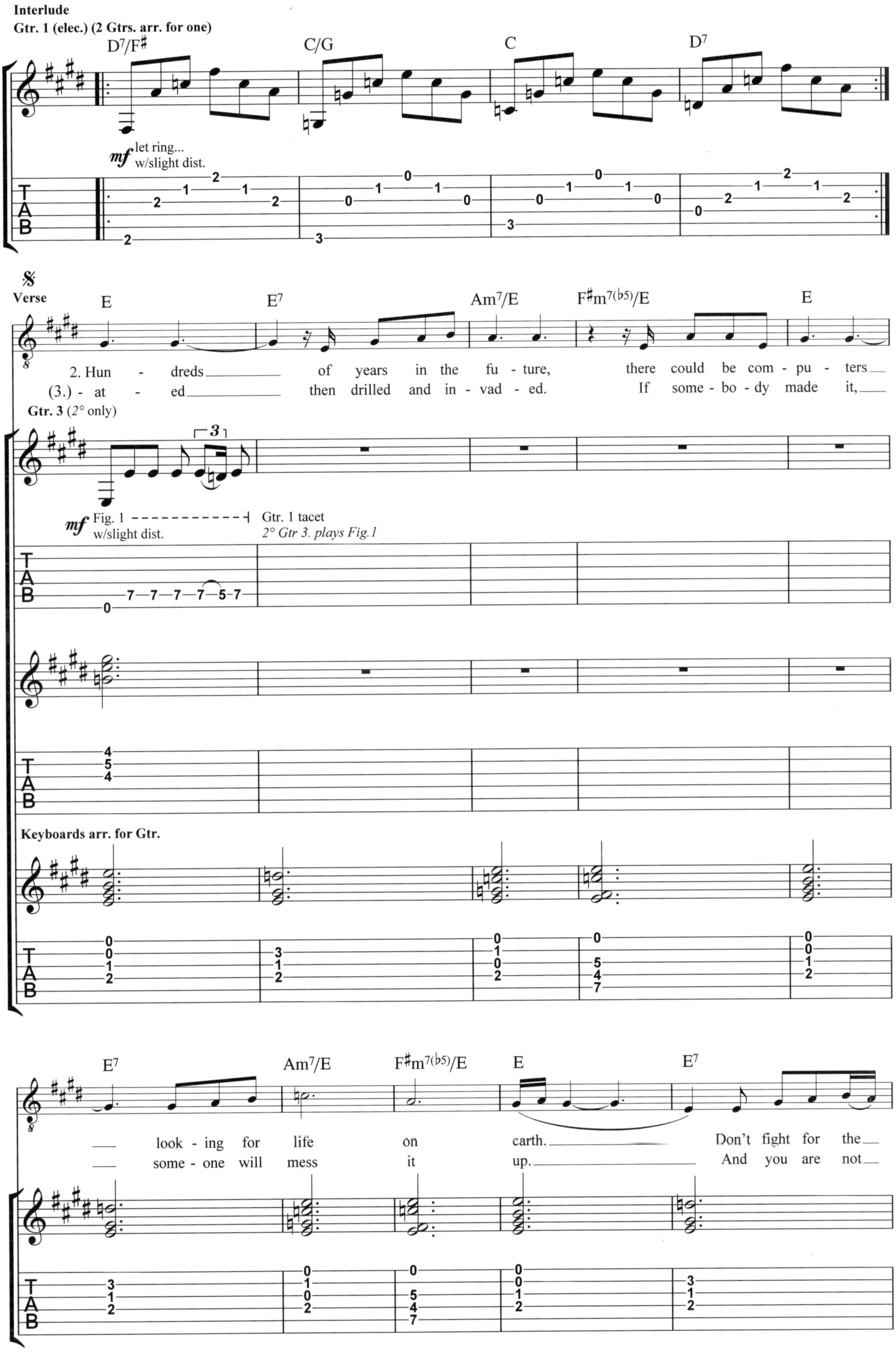
Interlude
Gtr. 1 (elec.) (2 Gtrs. arr. for one)
D7/F#
C/G
C
D7
mf let ring...
w/slight dist.
Verse
E
E7
Am7/E
F#m7(b5)/E
E
2. Hun - dreds of years in the fu - ture, there could be com - pu - ters
(3.) - at - ed then drilled and in - vad - ed. If some - bo - dy made it,
Gtr. 3 (2° only)
mf Fig. 1
w/slight dist.
Gtr. 1 tacet
2° Gtr 3. plays Fig. 1
Keyboards arr. for Gtr.
E7
Am7/E
F#m7(b5)/E
E
E7
look - ing for life on earth. Don't fight for the
some - one will mess it up. And you are not

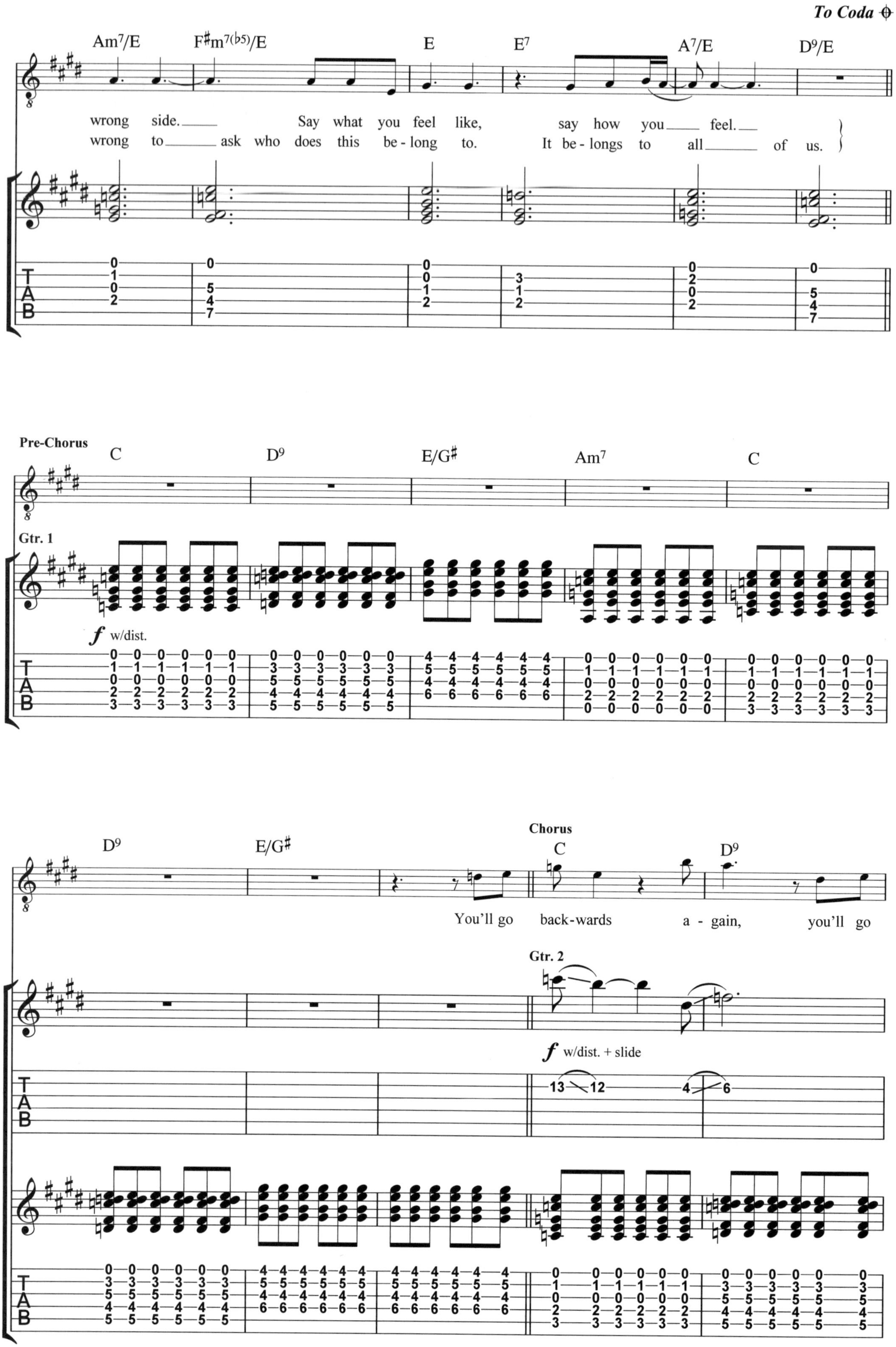
To Coda
Am7/E F#m7(b5)/E E E7 A7/E D9/E
wrong side. Say what you feel like, say how you feel.
wrong to ask who does this be - long to. It be - longs to all of us.
Pre-Chorus
C D9 E/G# Am7 C
Gtr. 1
f w/dist.
D9 E/G#
Chorus
C D9
You'll go back-wards a - gain, you'll go
Gtr. 2
f w/dist. + slide

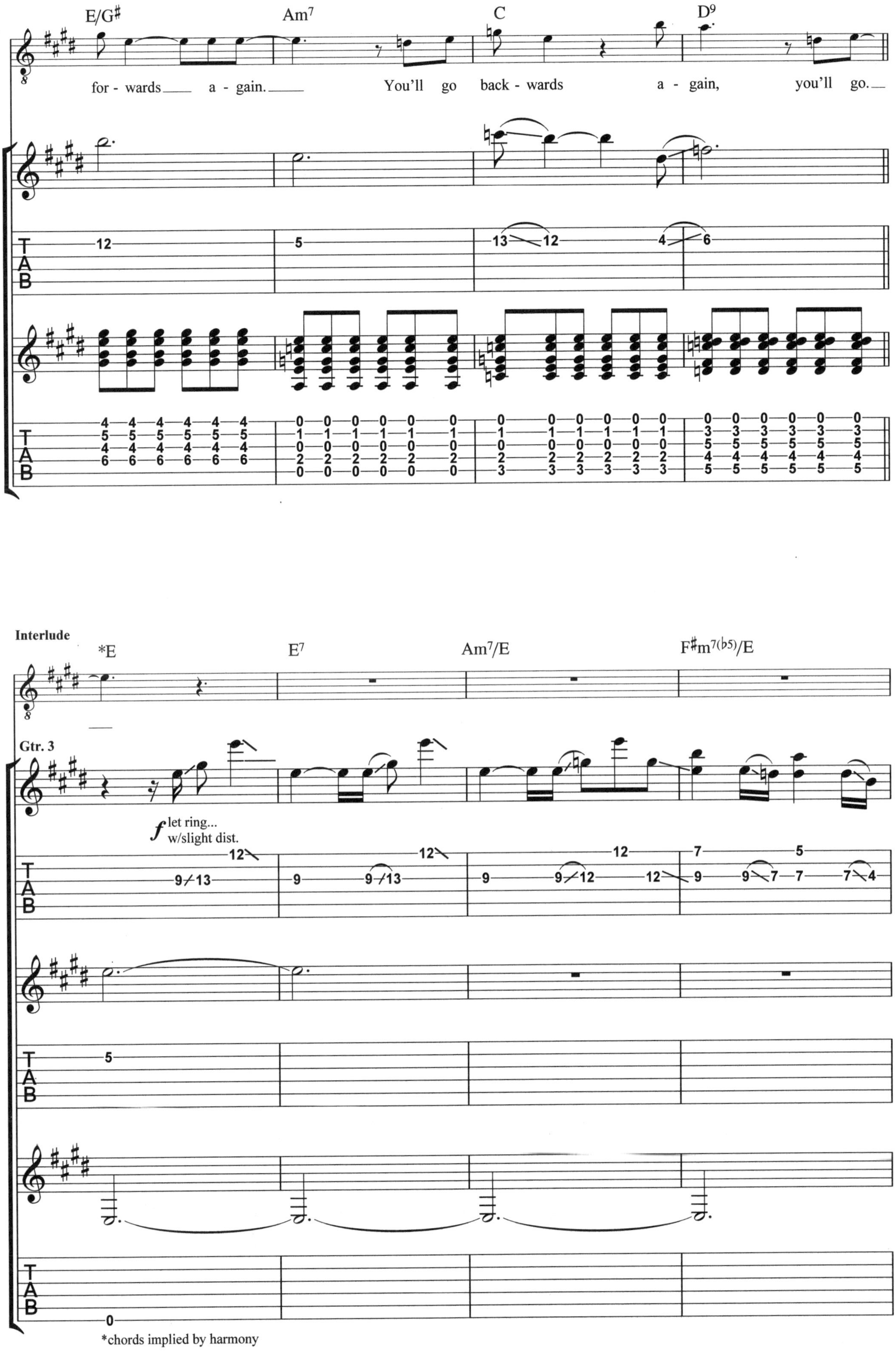
E/G♯
Am7
C
D9
for - wards a - gain. You'll go back - wards a - gain, you'll go.
Interlude
*E
E7
Am7/E
F♯m7(♭5)/E
Gtr. 3
f let ring...
w/slight dist.
*chords implied by harmony

E E7 Am7/E F♯m7(♭5)/E
D.S. al Coda
3. Cre -
Coda
Gtr. 3
D7/F♯ C/G C D7
Gtr. 1 (elec.) (2 Gtrs. arr. for one)
mf let ring...
w/slight dist.
E
Chorus
C D9 E/G♯
You'll go back - wards a - gain, you'll go for - wards a - gain.
Gtr. 2
f w/dist. + slide

Am7
C
D9
E/G
You'll go back- wards a - gain, you'll go for - wards. You'll go
T
A
B
5
13 12 12 4 6
9
0 0 0 0 0 0
1 1 1 1 1 1
0 0 0 0 0 0
2 2 2 2 2 2
0 0 0 0 0 0
cont. in slashes
Gtr. 1
cont. sim.
back - wards a - gain, you'll go
Gtr. 5
f w/dist.
full
E
for - wards a - gain.
You'll go

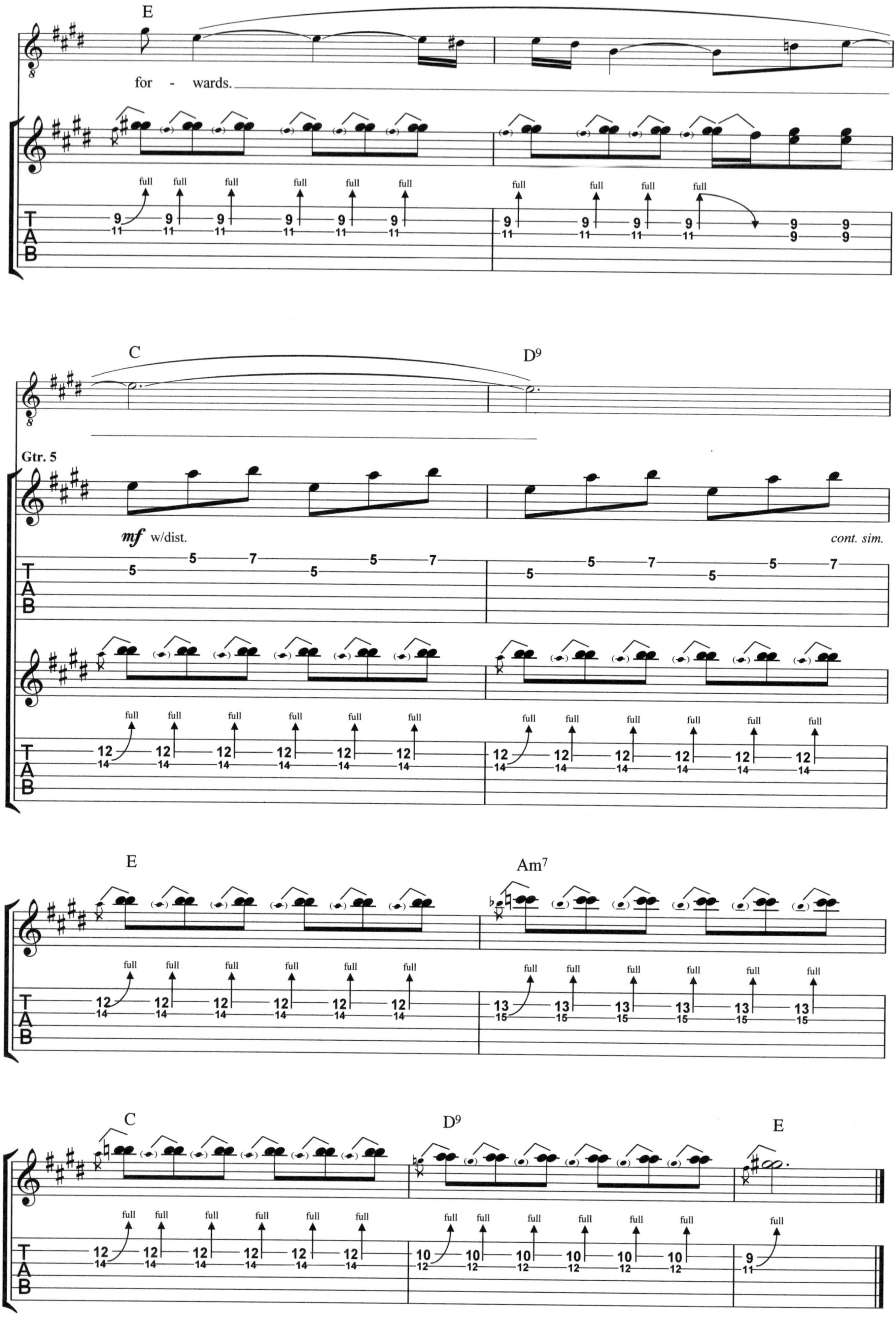
E
for - wards.
C
D9
Gtr. 5
mf w/dist.
cont. sim.
E
Am7
C
D9
E
full
TAB

TILL KINGDOM COME

Words & Music by Guy Berryman, Jon Buckland, Will Champion & Chris Martin

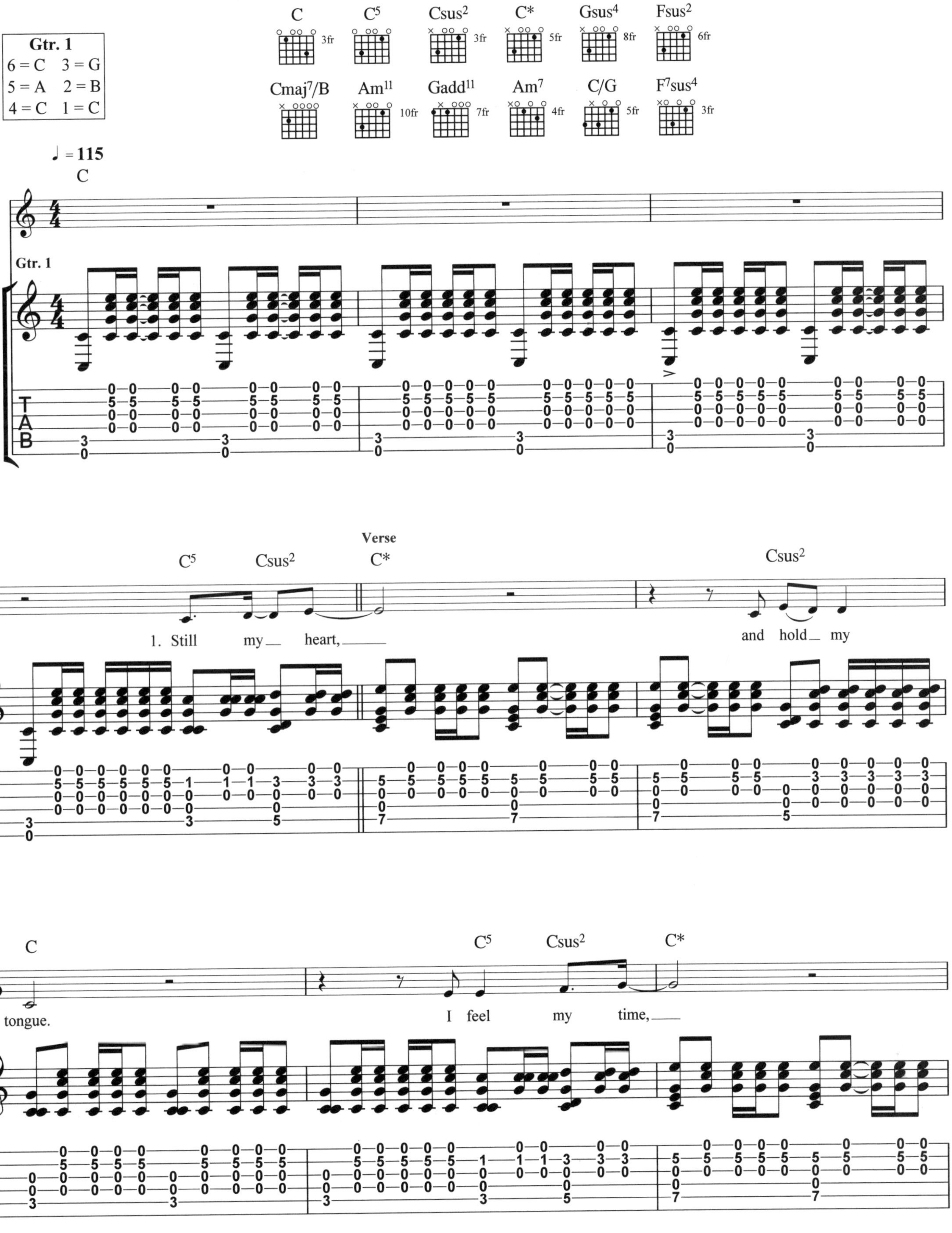

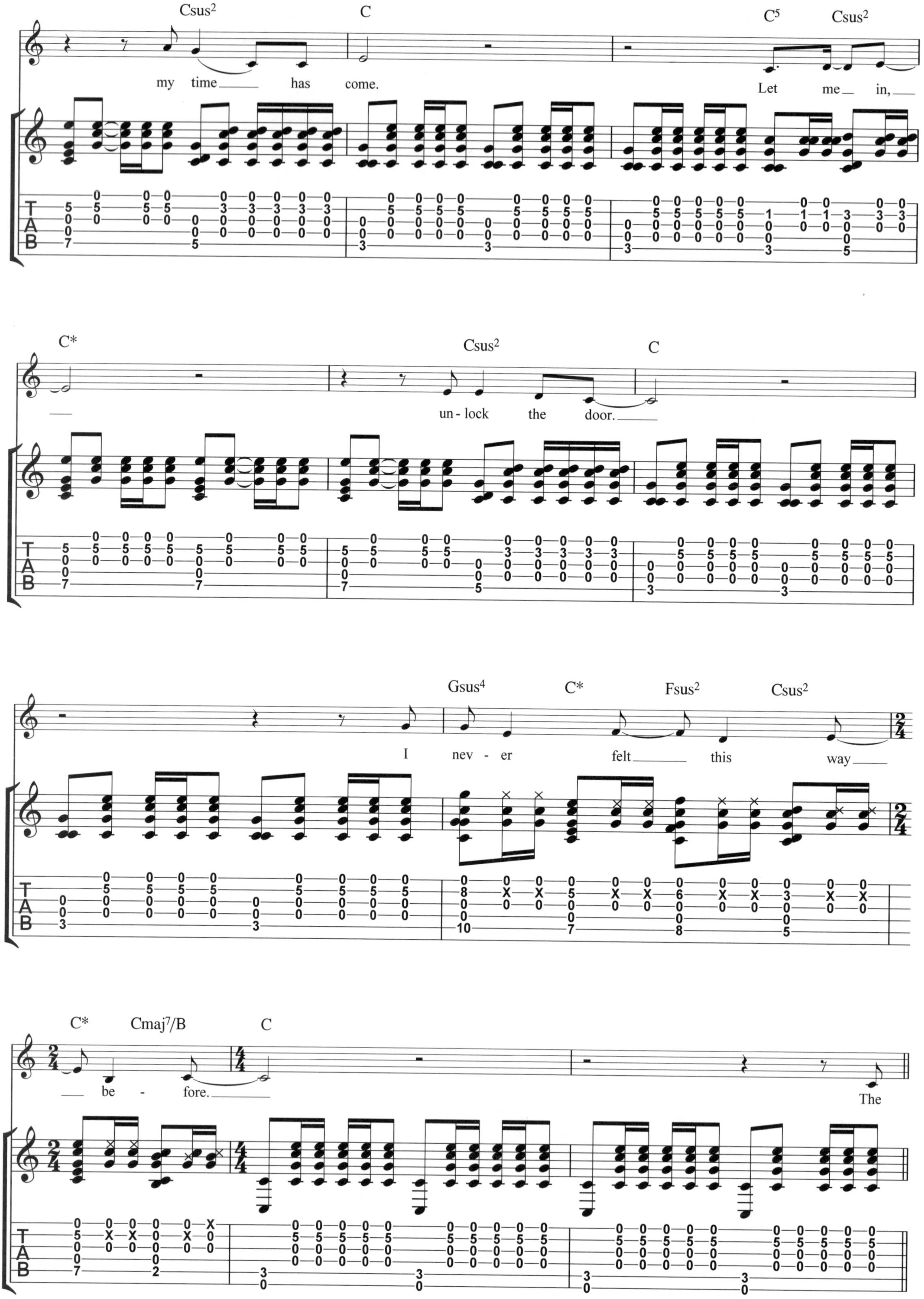
Csus2
C
C5
Csus2
my time has come.
Let me in,
C*
Csus2
C
un - lock the door.
Gsus4
C*
Fsus2
Csus2
I nev - er felt this way
C*
Cmaj7/B
C
be - fore.
The

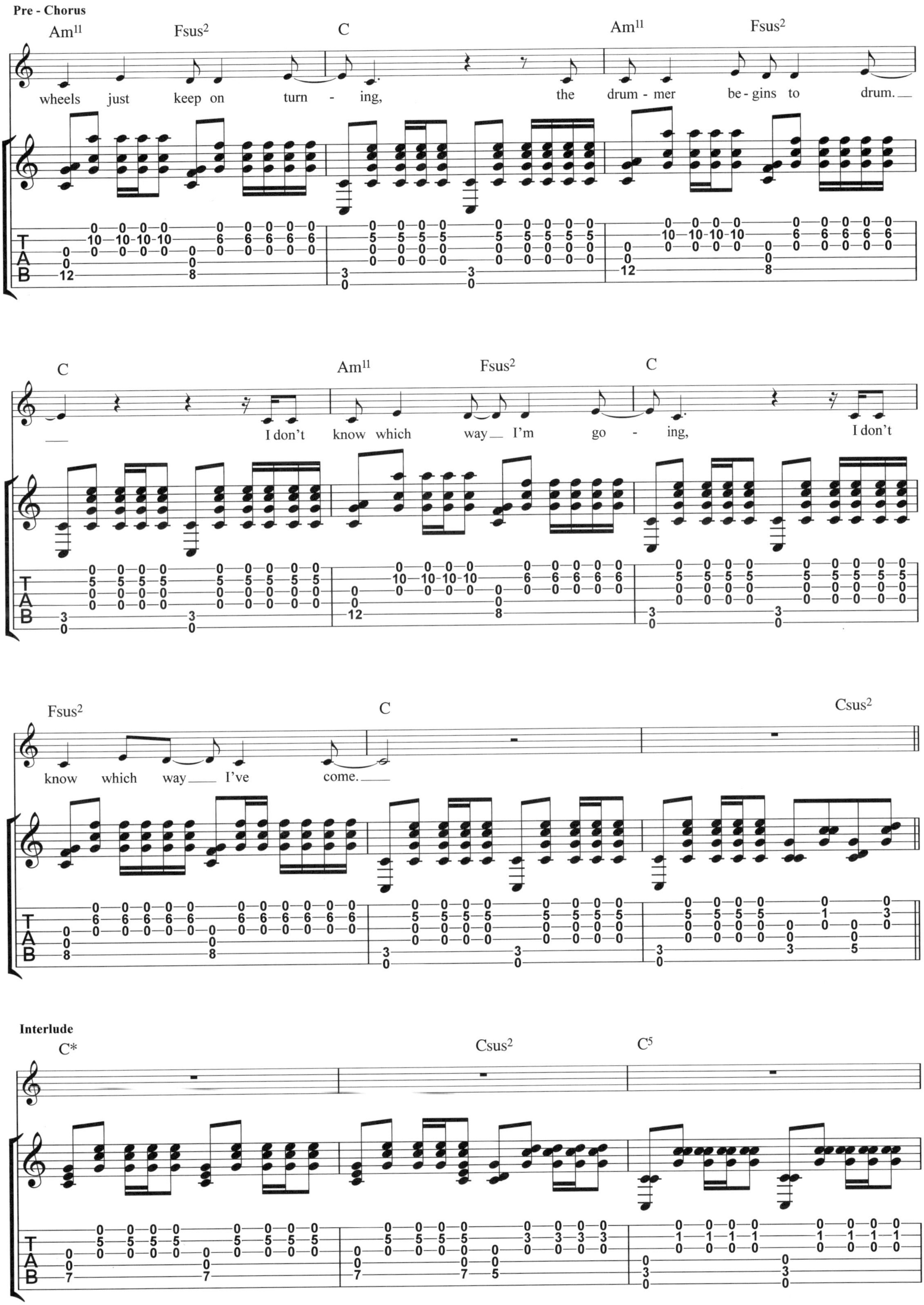
Pre - Chorus
Am11 Fsus2 C Am11 Fsus2
wheels just keep on turn - ing, the drum - mer be - gins to drum.
C Am11 Fsus2 C
I don't know which way I'm go - ing, I don't
Fsus2 C Csus2
know which way I've come.
Interlude
C* Csus2 C5
TAB

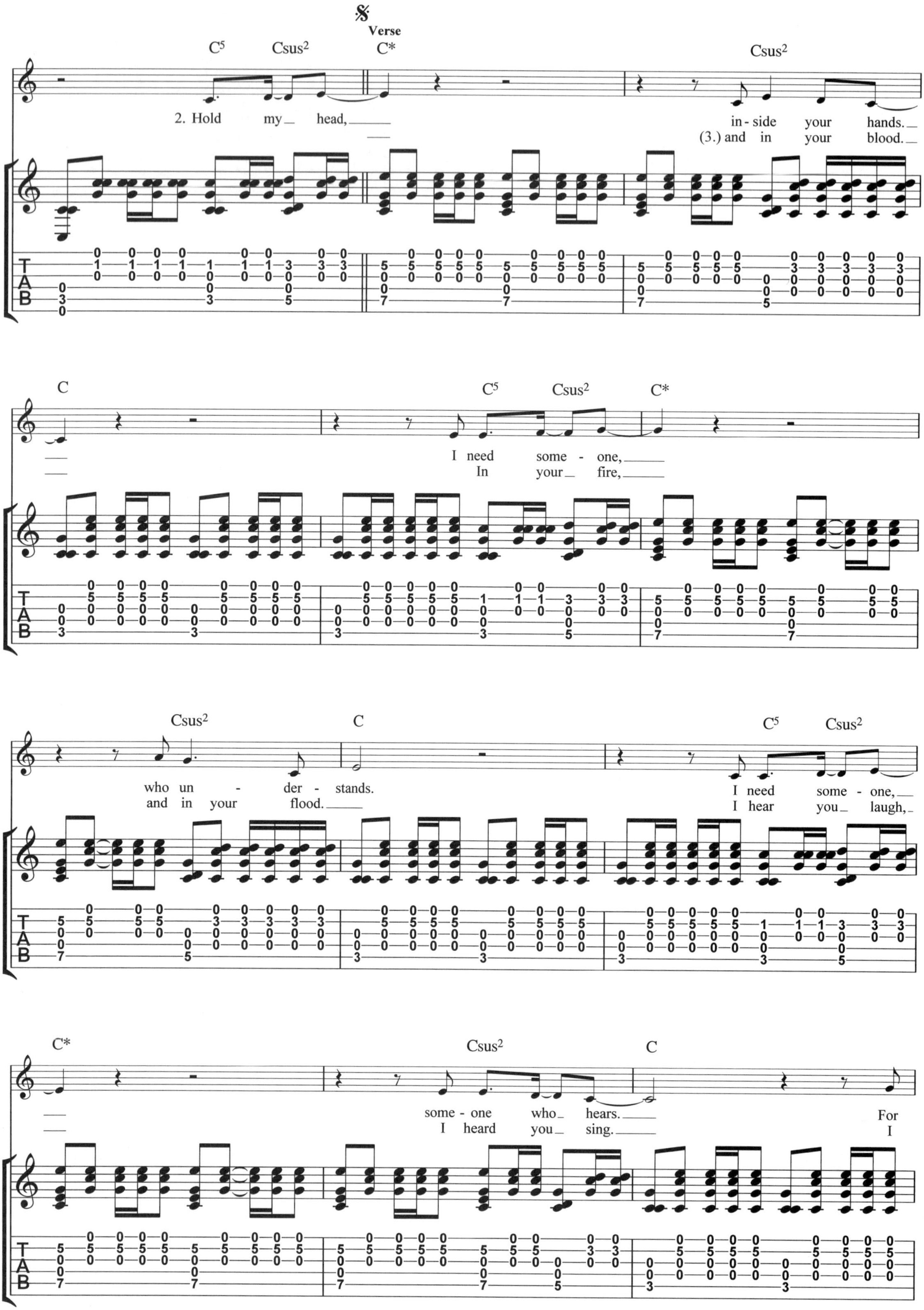
Verse
C5 Csus2 C* Csus2
2. Hold my head, in-side your hands.
(3.) and in your blood.
C C5 Csus2 C*
I need some - one,
In your fire,
Csus2 C C5 Csus2
who un - der - stands. I need some - one,
and in your flood. I hear you laugh,
C* Csus2 C
some - one who hears. For
I heard you sing. I
T
A
B

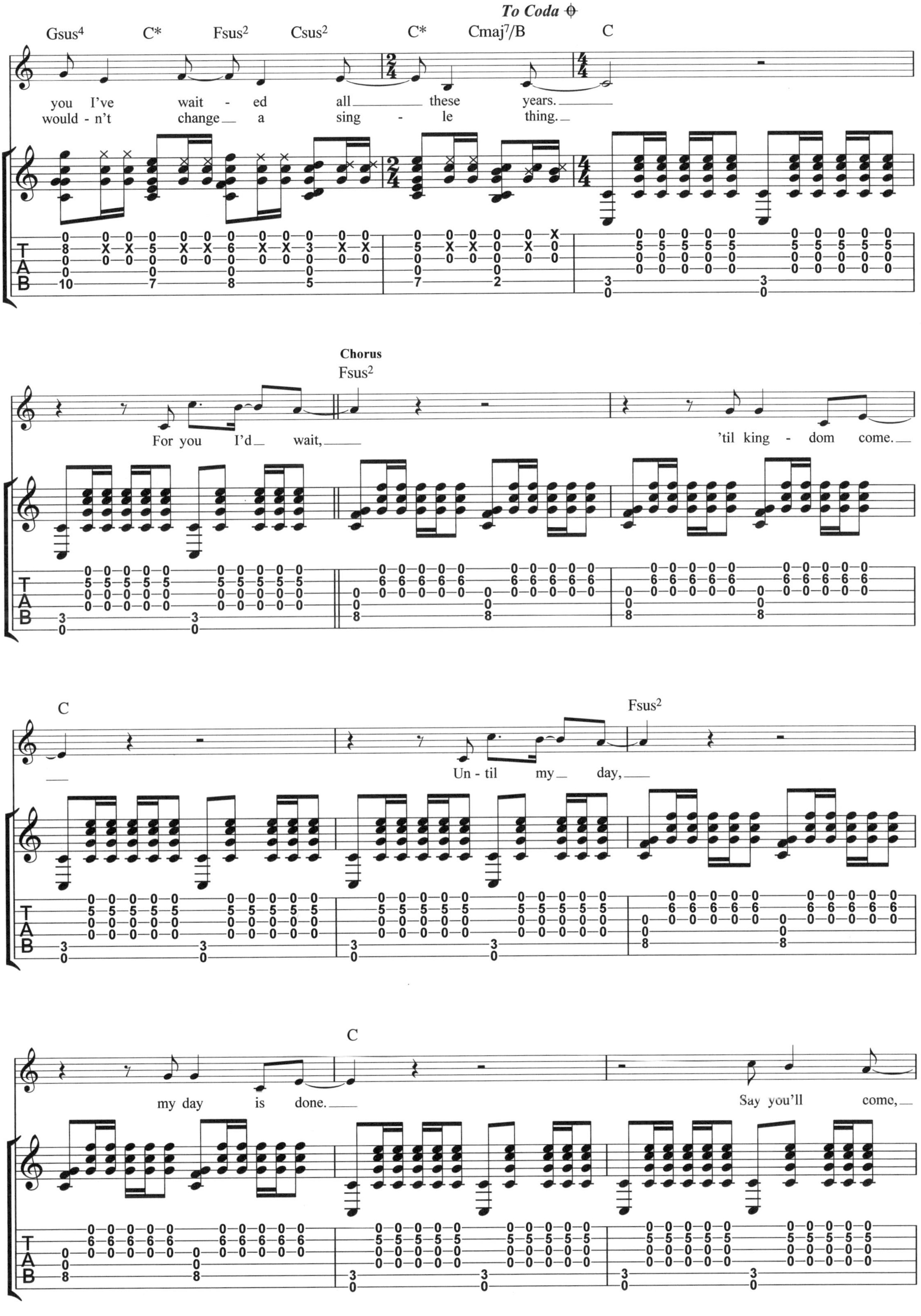
To Coda
Gsus4 C* Fsus2 Csus2 C* Cmaj7/B C
you I've wait - ed all these years.
would - n't change a sing - le thing.
Chorus
Fsus2
For you I'd wait, 'til king - dom come.
C Fsus2
Un - til my day,
C
my day is done. Say you'll come,
T
A
B

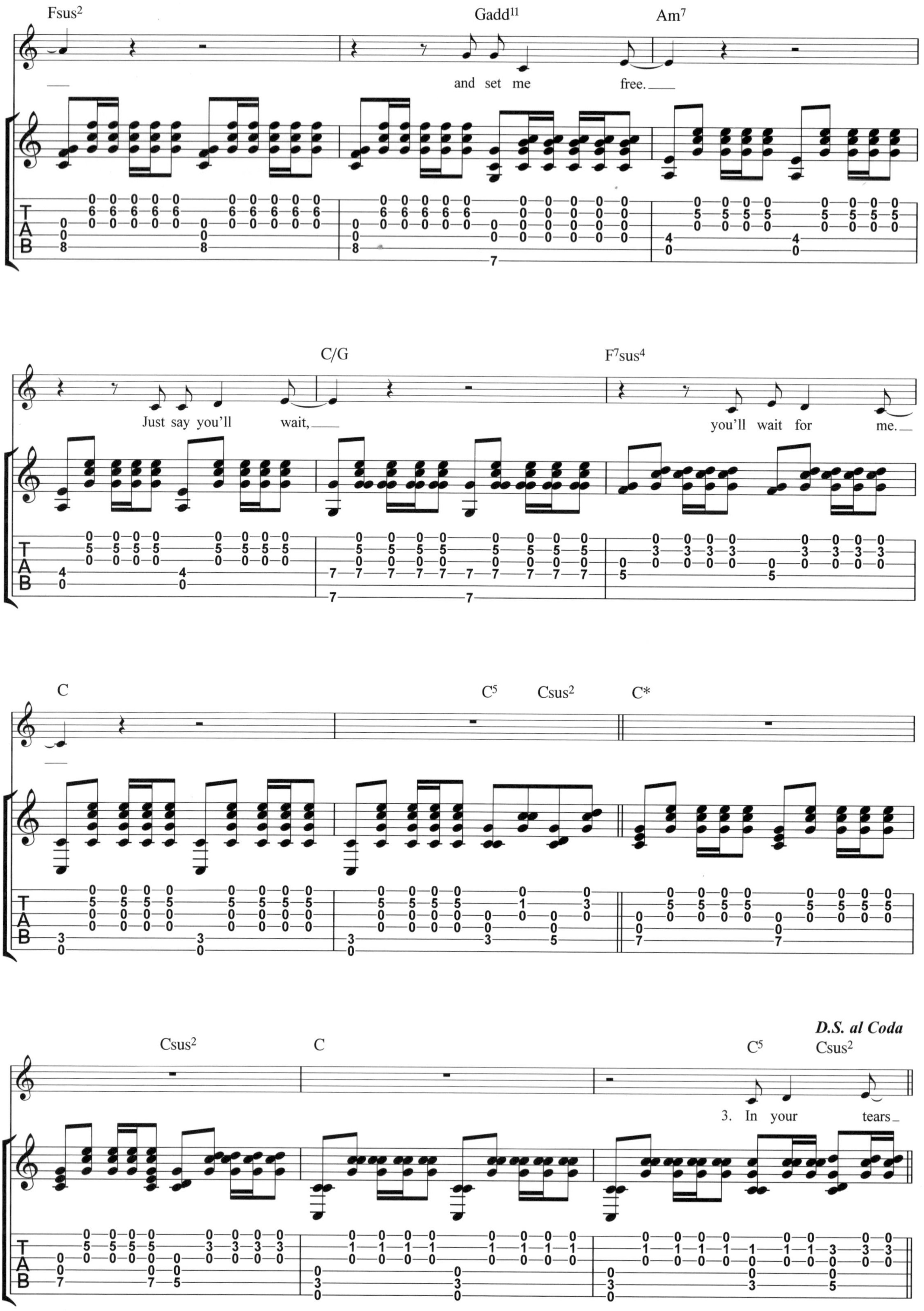
Fsus2
Gadd11
Am7
and set me free.
C/G
F7sus4
Just say you'll wait,
you'll wait for me.
C
C5
Csus2
C*
Csus2
C
D.S. al Coda
C5
Csus2
3. In your tears
TAB

Coda
Pre Chorus
C
Am11
Fsus2
The wheels just keep on turn -
C
Am11
Fsus2
- ing, the drum - mers be - gin to drum.
C
Am11
Fsus2
I don't know which way I'm go -
C
Fsus2
- ing, I don't know what I'll be - come.

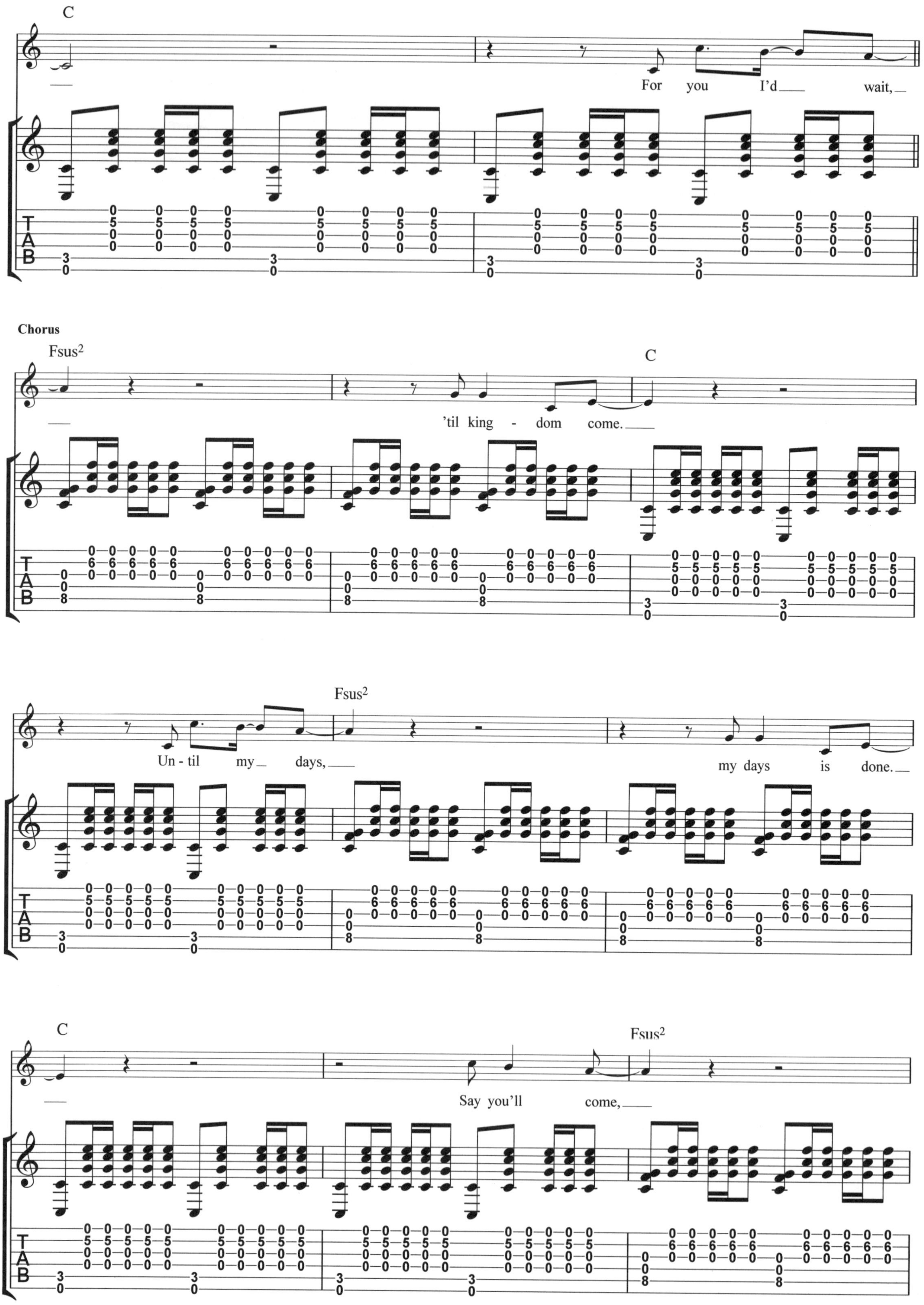
C
For you I'd wait,
Chorus
Fsus2
'til king - dom come.
C
Un - til my days,
Fsus2
my days is done.
C
Say you'll come,
Fsus2
T
A
B

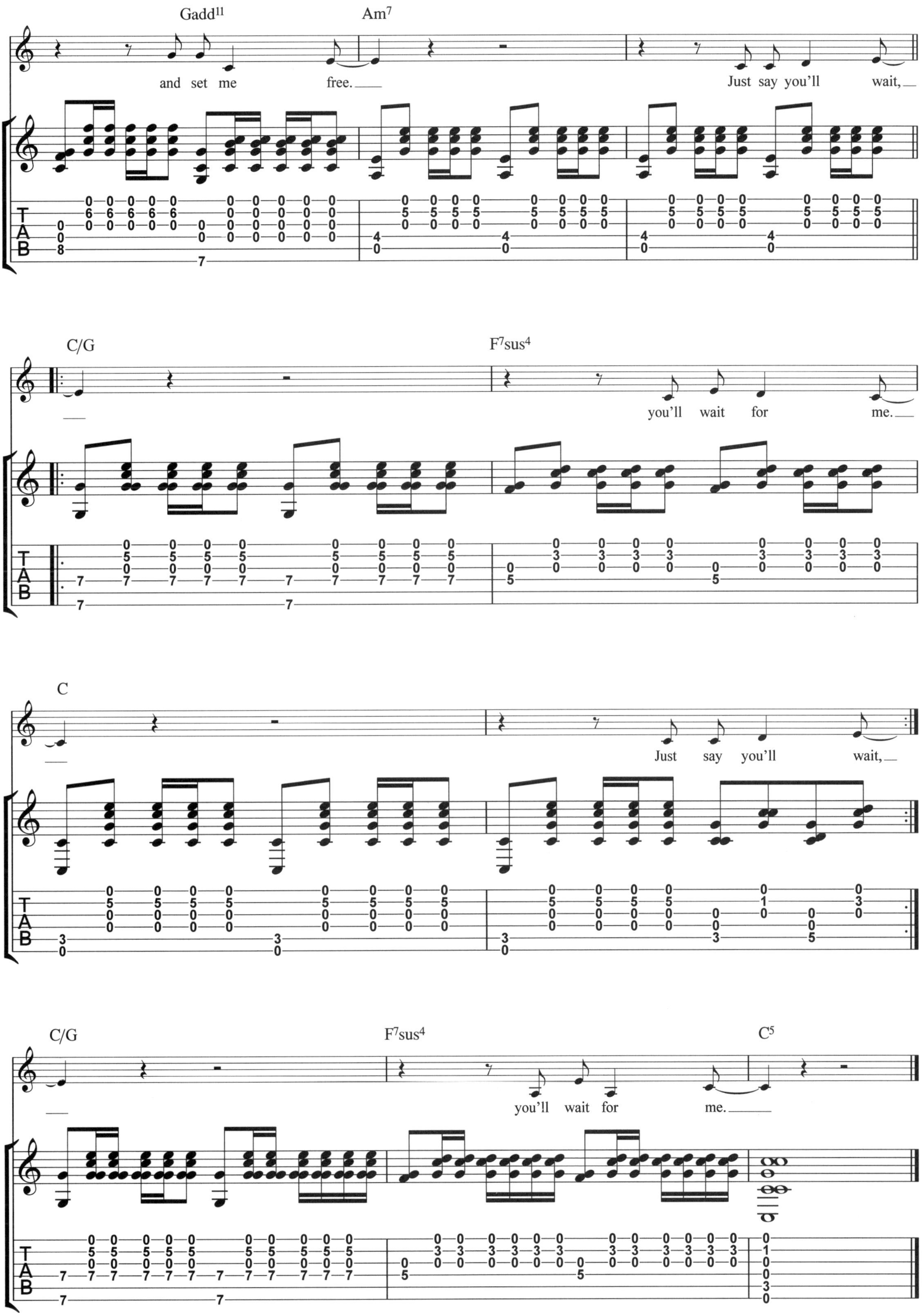
Gadd11
Am7
and set me free.
Just say you'll wait,
C/G
F7sus4
you'll wait for me.
C
Just say you'll wait,
C/G
F7sus4
C5
you'll wait for me.
TAB

Guitar Tablature Explained

Guitar music can be notated in three different ways: on a musical stave, in tablature, and in rhythm slashes.

RHYTHM SLASHES are written above the stave. Strum chords in the rhythm indicated. Round noteheads indicate single notes.

THE MUSICAL STAVE shows pitches and rhythms and is divided by lines into bars. Pitches are named after the first seven letters of the alphabet.

TABLATURE graphically represents the guitar fingerboard. Each horizontal line represents a string, and each number represents a fret.

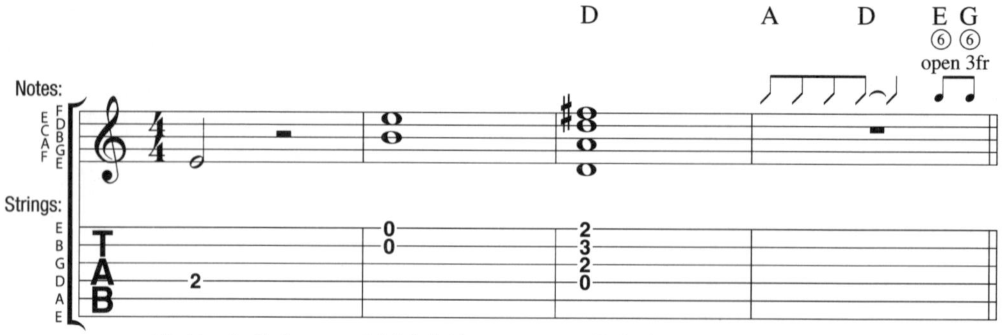

4th string, 2nd fret

1st & 2nd strings open, played together

open D chord

Definitions For Special Guitar Notation

SEMI-TONE BEND: Strike the note and bend up a semi-tone (1/2 step).

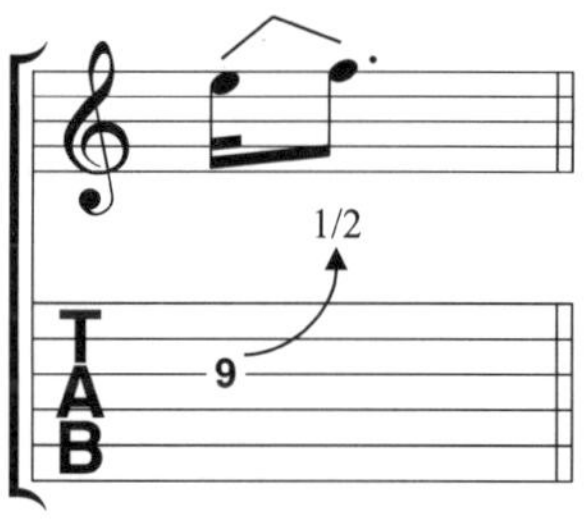

WHOLE-TONE BEND: Strike the note and bend up a whole-tone (whole step).

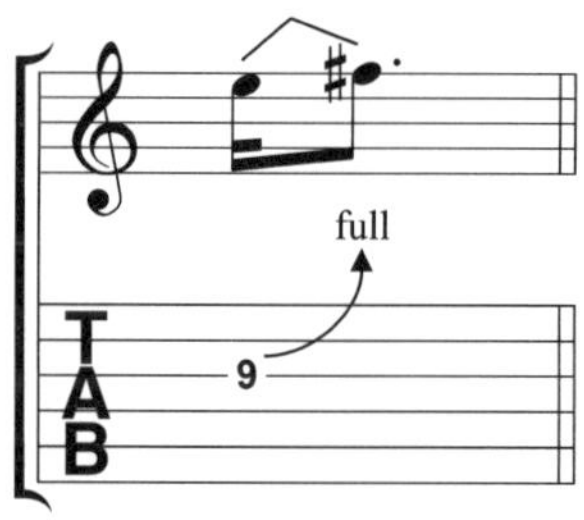

GRACE NOTE BEND: Strike the note and bend as indicated. Play the first note as quickly as possible.

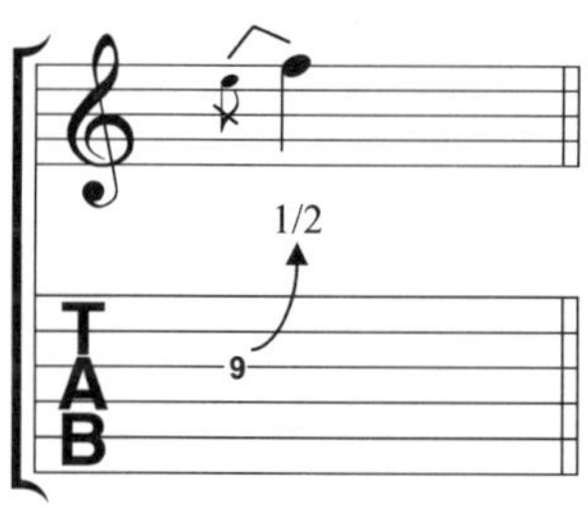

QUARTER-TONE BEND: Strike the note and bend up a 1/4 step.

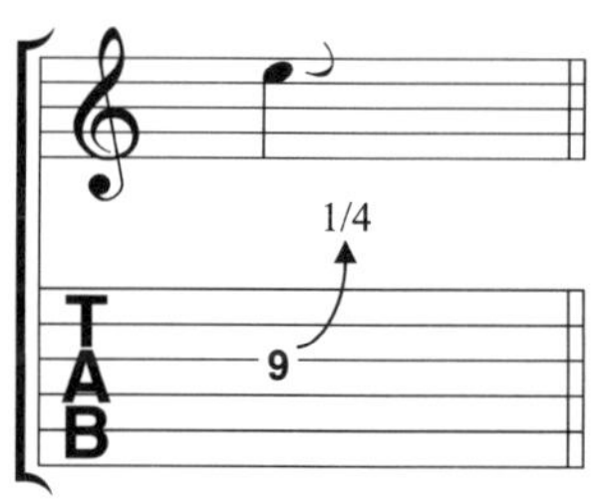

BEND & RELEASE: Strike the note and bend up as indicated, then release back to the original note.

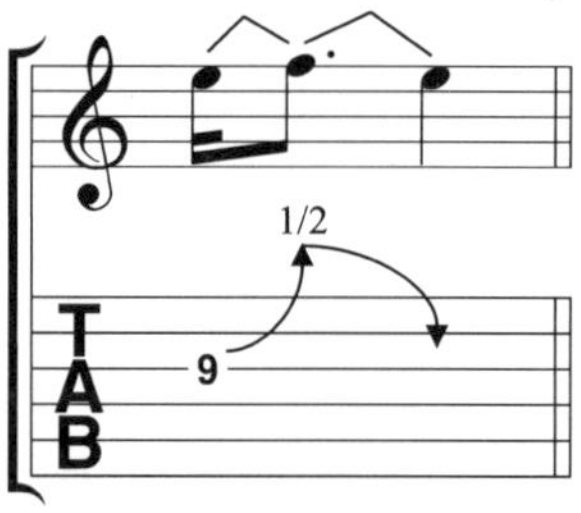

COMPOUND BEND & RELEASE: Strike the note and bend up and down in the rhythm indicated.

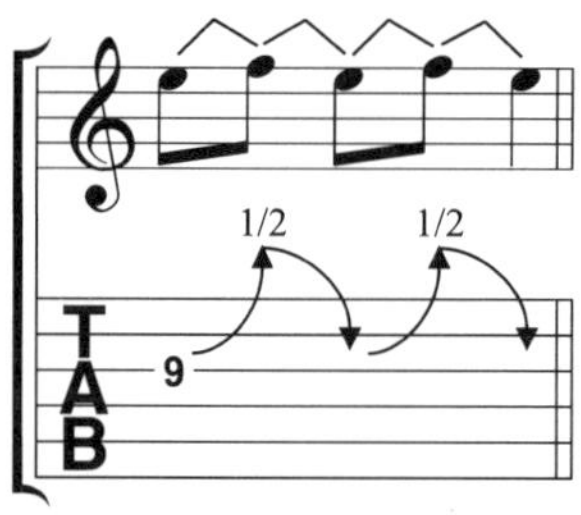

PRE-BEND: Bend the note as indicated, then strike it.

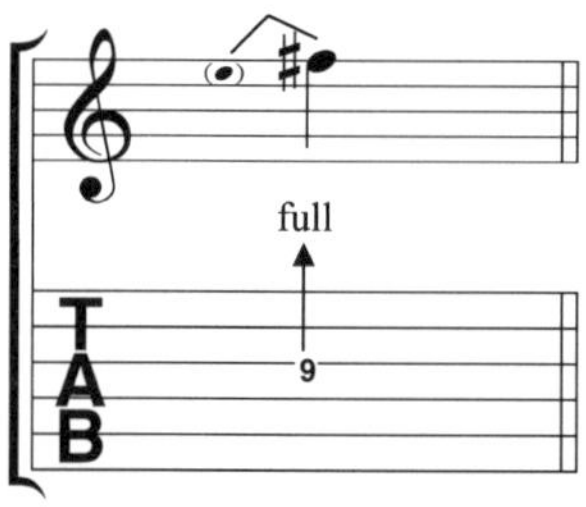

PRE-BEND & RELEASE: Bend the note as indicated. Strike it and release the note back to the original pitch.

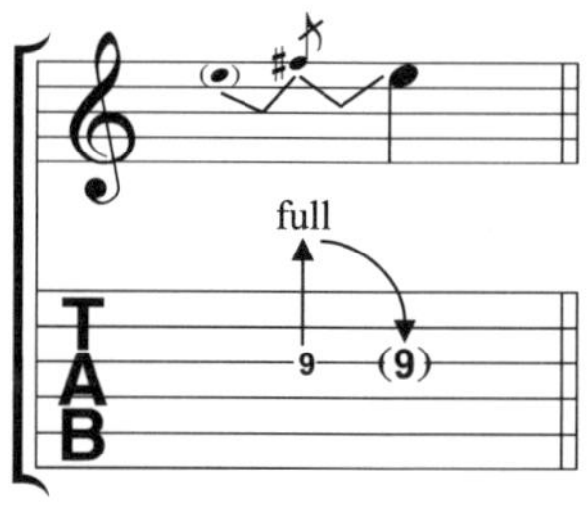

HAMMER-ON: Strike the first note with one finger, then sound the second note (on the same string) with another finger by fretting it without picking.

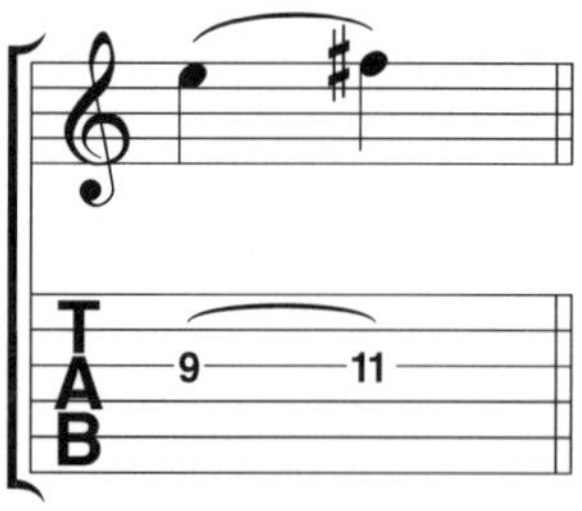

PULL-OFF: Place both fingers on the notes to be sounded, strike the first note and without picking, pull the finger off to sound the second note.

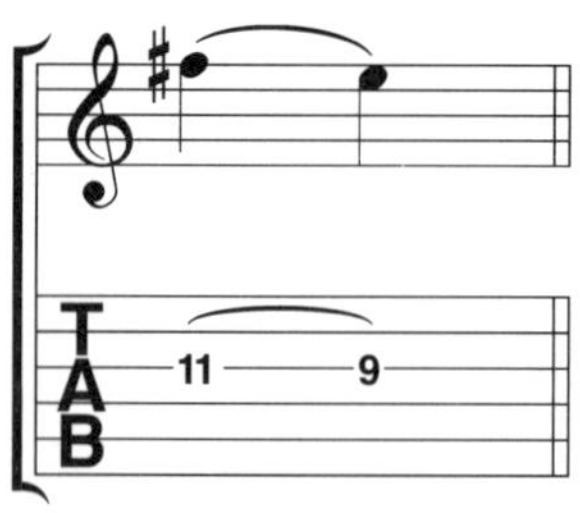

LEGATO SLIDE (GLISS): Strike the first note and then slide the same fret-hand finger up or down to the second note. The second note is not struck.

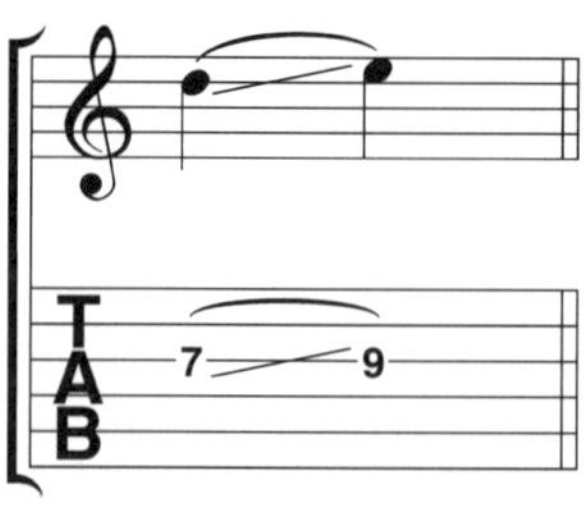

MUFFLED STRINGS: A percussive sound is produced by laying the fret hand across the string(s) without depressing, and striking them with the pick hand.

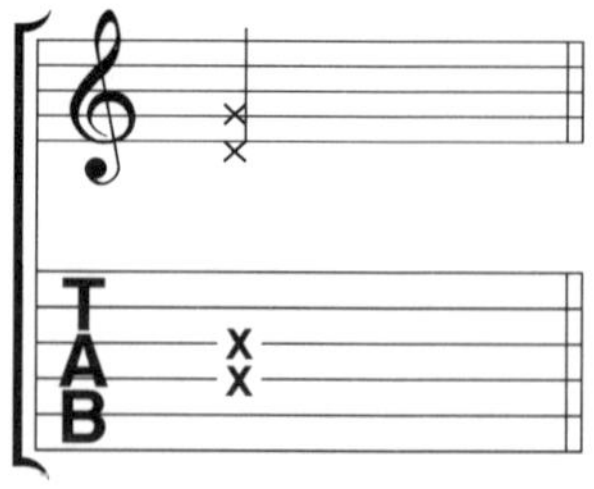

NATURAL HARMONIC: Strike the note while the fret-hand lightly touches the string directly over the fret indicated.

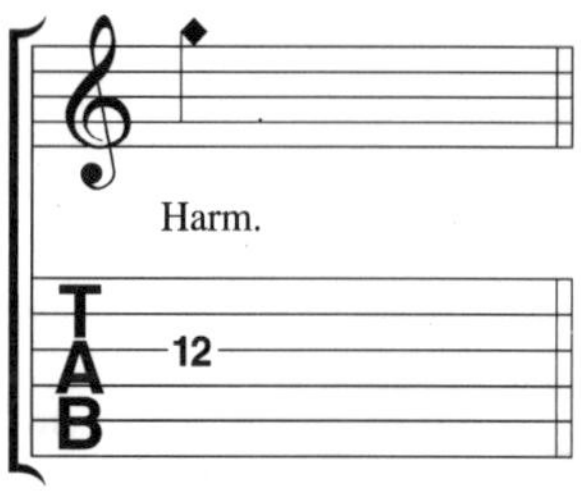

PICK SCRAPE: The edge of the pick is rubbed down (or up) the string, producing a scratchy sound.

PALM MUTING: The note is partially muted by the pick hand lightly touching the string(s) just before the bridge.

SHIFT SLIDE (GLISS & RESTRIKE): Same as legato slide, except the second note is struck.

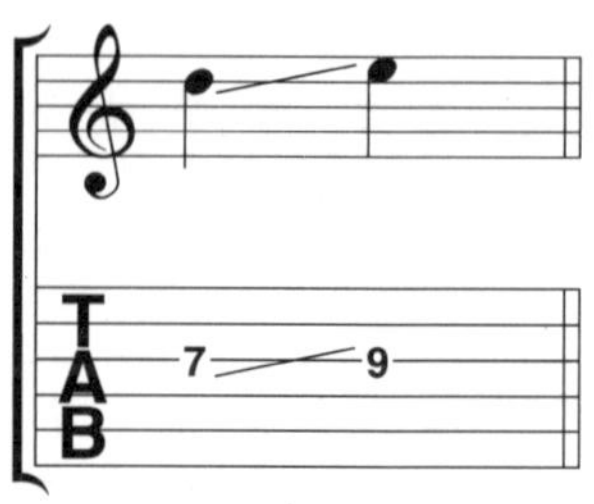

NOTE: The speed of any bend is indicated by the music notation and tempo.

1 2 3 4 5 6 7 8 9